M
1629
.C2
F7

Carawan

Freedom is a constant
struggle

0

FREEDOM IS A CONSTANT STRUGGLE
Songs of the Freedom Movement

ALSO BY GUY AND CANDIE CARAWAN

We Shall Overcome - Songs of the Southern Freedom Struggle.

Ain't You Got A Right to the Tree of Life? The people of Johns Island, South Carolina.

Recordings

Greenwood, Mississippi Story

Freedom in the Air - Albany, Georgia

Nashville Sit-In Story

We Shall Overcome: Southern Freedom Songs

Been In The Storm So Long

Moving Star Hall Singers

FREEDOM IS A CONSTANT STRUGGLE
Songs of the Freedom Movement

COMPILED AND EDITED BY GUY AND CANDIE CARAWAN
WITH DOCUMENTARY PHOTOGRAPHS / MUSIC TRANSCRIPTIONS BY ETHEL RAIM

OAK PUBLICATIONS, NEW YORK, N.Y.

Book Design by Ken Thompson and Jean Hammons

SECOND PRINTING

All songs, unless previously copyrighted, are copyright ©1968
on behalf of the author by Oak Publications.

©1968 by OAK PUBLICATIONS
A Division of Embassy Music Corporation
33 West 60th Street, New York 10023

Library of Congress Card Catalogue Number: 67-27261

Printed in the United States of America for the Publisher by Faculty Press, Inc., Brooklyn, N. Y. 199

ACKNOWLEDGEMENTS

We would like to gratefully acknowledge permission granted to quote from the following books: "The Martyrs" by Jack Mendelsoh, published by Harper and Row; "SNCC: The New Abolitionists" by Howard Zinn, published by Beacon Press; "Letters from Mississippi" edited by Elizabeth Sutherland, published by McGraw-Hill; "Mississippi Notebook" by Nicholas Von Hoffman, published by David White Company.

Acknowledgements also to the following writers: Pat Watters in "New South"; Margaret Long in "The Progrssive"; Lerone Bennett Jr. in "SNCC: Rebels With A Cause"; Henry Hampton in "To Bear Witness"; Ann Braden in "The Southern Patriot"; David Llorens in "Sing Out!"; Elizabeth Sutherland in "The Nation"; Martin Luther King Jr. in "The Progressive"; writers of The National Council of Churches in "Reports".

ROYALTIES AND GRANTS

The authors' royalties from this book are being donated to the Freedom Movement through the Freedom Fund -- a fund dedicated to helping develop the music of the movement and an awareness of its roots.

We would like to thank the Freedom Fund (administered by the Highlander Research & Education Center, Knoxville, Tenn.) for a grant that made it possible for us to do this book.

CONTENTS

INTRODUCTION

"No more long prayers, no more Freedom songs, no more dreams -- let's go for power."

Stokely Carmichael, 1966

Here is a book of Freedom songs -- songs that have evolved since the 1963 March on Washington.* Already many of them seem out-dated in light of the new mood within the Civil Rights Movement. The days of singing "we love everybody... we love Gov. Wallace" have passed. Many battle scarred veterans of the last six years can no longer stand with arms crossed and sing with great hope and expectation that "the truth will make us free." Julius Lester in the epilogue to this book predicts that "the days of singing freedom songs and the days of combating bullets and billy clubs with love are over. 'We Shall Overcome' sounds old, out-dated. 'Man, the people are too busy getting ready to fight to bother with singing any more!'" It remains to be seen if his prediction is correct. Will Freedom songs really pass from the scene or will new songs evolve to meet new needs? Will mass singing play an important role in new developments as it has in the past?

Since 1960 singing has been important to the movement. People sang on demonstrations and at mass meetings, in paddy wagons and jail cells, to bolster spirits, to gain courage and to bring people together. Every new chapter of the struggle produced its own songs. This book documents that process.

Birmingham, St. Augustine, Danville, Atlanta, Americus and elsewhere -- campaign after campaign carried on the traditions of a singing movement. New songs were written; old ones adapted. The 1964 Mississippi Summer Project left behind its songs, more diversified because of the participation of a thousand outsiders including northern song-writers. The Selma March in the Spring of 1965 brought attention to a growing movement in the black belt of Alabama. The fifty mile march was very conducive to the spontaneous improvisation of verse after verse after verse. Many songs got started there and carried elsewhere by the 40,000 marchers from all across the country. The march ended in front of the state capitol in Montgomery in a powerful show of "black and white together... we shall overcome" and will surely go down as a turning point -- perhaps the last time that such a scene will be witnessed in this country for some time to come.

---

* For the Freedom songs of the period of the Sit-ins, Freedom Rides and the early Voter Registration drives, see We Shall Overcome - Oak Publications, 1963.

In 1966 there would be another march which, by its end, was almost all Negro and ringing with a new cry -- "Black Power!" The Mississippi March began after the shooting of James Meredith and soon became a walking forum for Negro leaders discussing the merits of an all-black movement. There was dissention and argument but it was clear to everyone that it was a time of change. At least two new songs were heard expressing the new mood -- Len Chandler's angry "Move on Over or We'll Move on Over You' and Jimmy Collier's "Burn, Baby, Burn".

"Burn, Baby, Burn" emerged when the Civil Rights Movement went north. Jimmy Collier, a young song-writer and organizer with Dr. King's End the Slum campaign in Chicago, wrote it in response to the Watts Riots. A number of other new songs expressive of northern ghetto life have come out of the Chicago Movement. Many of them are based on rock & roll and rhythm & blues rather than spiritual and gospel songs. It should be noted that Dr. King and his co-workers are trying to keep their movement non-violent and so far most of these new songs are in that vein. (But they are having a hard time convincing many ghetto dwellers who agree with a veteran of Watts when he declares "folk singing is out...karate is in.")

An important part of the new mood within the movement is a proud embracing of American Negro folk heritage and its earlier African roots. There have been a number of festivals and conferences exploring this much neglected heritage. The excitement this has generated is spreading and is reflected in such diverse things as clothing, natural hair styles, a new interest in folk ways and a respect for the folk qualities of a great leader like Mrs. Fannie Lou Hamer. Included in this development is a growing awareness and appreciation of Negro folk music. That is why we have included a chapter on the roots -- old spirituals, children's songs, worksongs and blues -- songs that have sung of freedom and protested in their own way, some of them since slavery times.

Since 1960 there have been tremendous changes in the Civil Rights Movement. The veterans of those six years have experienced disillusionment and growth. With the new demand of Black Power they are trying to grapple with more realistic ways to change our society. They now know for certain it will take more than Love, Courage and Truth. Those same people who created and sang the songs of love and brotherhood, now parody them in jest and seek for new ways of expression. ("Too much love, too much love, nothing kills the movement like too much love.")

Just as they were once willing to use non-violent direct action as a tactic to achieve changes in American society, many are now willing to encourage violence in the form of ghetto riots to achieve those changes. For the most disillusioned have come to feel that nothing short of the threat of destructive violence and the wounding of America will force her to look deeply at the poverty and despair in her ghettoes and rural slums and deal with the problems.

Just what forms of expression, musical or otherwise, will accompany these new developments must be left to some future book.

Guy & Candie Carawan

NOTES ON THE SONGS

The song versions in this book should not be taken as absolutely definitive. Many of these words and tunes are sung with some variation from area to area and person to person. Words are often adapted to new situations and new verses ad-libbed on the spot. Also the improvisational style in which they are sung cannot be completely captured by orthodox musical notation. A good singer will subtly vary the tune -- bending notes, delaying or anticipating the beat, and adding his own vocal decorations.

Pete Seeger has said:

"One woman on the Selma march saw me trying to notate a melody, and said with a smile 'Don't you know you can't write down freedom songs?' -- which has been said by everyone who ever tried to capture Negro folk music with European music notation. All I can do is repeat what my father once told me: 'A folksong in a book is like a photograph of a bird in flight.'"

I GOT ON MY TRAVELLING SHOES

Birmingham
St. Augustine
Danville
Atlanta
Americus
and elsewhere

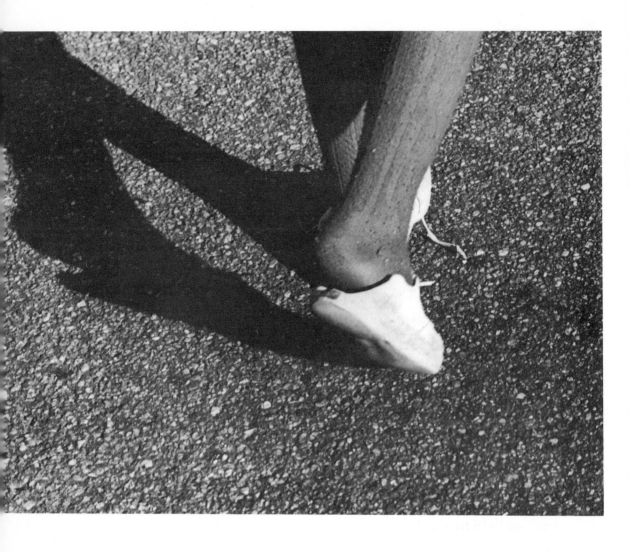

Travelling Shoes

Adaptation of spiritual Birmingham choir

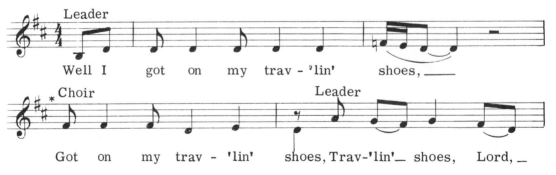

Leader

Well I got on my trav - 'lin' shoes, ___

Choir ＊   Leader

Got on my trav - 'lin' shoes, Trav-'lin'___ shoes, Lord, __

* Almost all the F♯ s are sung between F and F♯.

CHOIR	LEAD
Got on my travellin' shoes (2x)	Well I got on my travellin' shoes
Got on my travellin' shoes (2x)	I been travellin', Lord
Got on my travellin' shoes (2x)	Travellin' for freedom now
Got on my travellin' shoes (2x)	Fightin' for justice now
Got on my travellin' shoes (2x)	Don't you worry now
Got on my travellin' shoes (2x)	Travellin' shoes on

Birmingham, Alabama, 1963, became a major turning point in the civil rights movement. Thousands of local citizens, facing high pressure fire hoses and snarling police dogs, demonstrated. Over 3400 people, including 2000 students, went to jail. Developments in Birmingham triggered demonstrations in cities across the nation, creating the pressure which eventually produced the 1964 civil rights bill.

Great Day For Me

Adaptation of gospel song Birmingham choir

The sixty-voice Birmingham Movement gospel choir rocked mass meetings, making spirits jubilant, night after night for nearly three months.

	LEAD	CHOIR
Great day for me, great day for me,	Great day for me	Great day for me
I'm so happy, I want to be free	Oh yes it is	Great day for me
Since Jesus came to Birmingham	I am so happy	I'm so happy
I'm happy as can be,	I'm going to be	I'm going to be
Oh...oh, great day for me.	free	free
		Since Jesus came to Birmingham
	Oh	I'm happy as can be
	Oh yes	Oh...oh, great day for me.

Birmingham Sunday

The accomplishments of Birmingham have not been gained without great pain.

"On Sunday morning, September 15, 1963, Claude Wesley stood chatting with the attendant who was filling his car's gas tank at a service station two blocks from the 16th Street Baptist Church. All at once the whole morning exploded. Hurled by the force of ten or fifteen sticks of dynamite, rocks and glass crashed like shells through the trees, and Wesley, fighting to deny himself what he knew had happened, raced toward the screams which were rising from the church.

'... Love your enemies, bless them that curse you, do good to them that hate you, and pray for them which despitefully use you, and persecute you' was the text for that morning.

As the bomb detonated and rafters buckled, the teacher shreiked, "Lie on the floor! Lie on the floor!' Even as she screamed, the face of Jesus in the church's prized stained-glass window shattered into fragments."

Four young girls, including Claude Wesley's daughter, were dead.

Jack Mendelsohn, The Martyrs

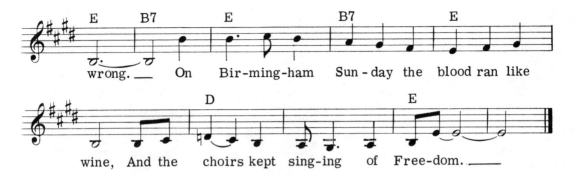

wrong. ___ On Bir-ming-ham Sun-day the blood ran like wine, And the choirs kept sing-ing of Free-dom. ___

Come round by my side and I'll sing you a song.
I'll sing it so softly, it'll do no one wrong.
On Birmingham Sunday the blood ran like wine,
And the choirs kept singing of Freedom.

That cold autumn morning no eyes saw the sun,
And Addie Mae Collins, her number was one.
At an old Baptist church there was no need to run.
And the choirs kept singing of Freedom.

The clouds they were grey and the autumn winds blew,
And Denise McNair brought the number to two.
The falcon of death was a creature they knew,
And the choirs kept singing of Freedom.

The church it was crowded, but no one could see
That Cynthia Wesley's dark number was three.
Her prayers and her feelings would shame you and me.
And the choirs kept singing of Freedom.

Young Carol Robertson entered the door
And the number her killers had given was four.
She asked for a blessing but asked for no more,
And the choirs kept singing of Freedom.

On Birmingham Sunday a noise shook the ground.
And people all over the earth turned around.
For no one recalled a more cowardly sound.
And the choirs kept singing of Freedom.

The men in the forest they once asked of me,
How many black berries grew in the Blue Sea.
And I asked them right back with a tear in my eye.
How many dark ships in the forest?

The Sunday has come and the Sunday has gone.
And I can't do much more than to sing you a song.
I'll sing it so softly, It'll do no one wrong.
And the choirs keep singing of Freedom.

We've Got A Job

Music and words:
Carlton Reese & B'ham choir

In 1966, the issue in Birmingham was voting. The demand was that registration be conducted in neighborhoods where Negroes live, and at night instead of only at the courthouse at hours inconvenient to working people. "We want the Courthouse brought out to the people", said Fred Shuttlesworth. As a result of many marches, federal registrars have now been sent to Birmingham. It is the first time they have been sent to an urban area where the Negro vote will have real power.

This is another of the freedom gospel songs of the Birmingham Movement Choir written by its organist-director, Carlton Reese.

I've got a job, I've got a job, and I want you to know,
you've got a job, all of God's chil-dren, all of God's chil-dren,
sure - ly, sure-ly got a job, we've got a job, ___
we've got a job to do, ___ we can't get free-dom 'til
we get through, car-ryin' the cross of our Lord.
We are fight-ing for free - dom, ___ come on, you

might not hear us free - dom. free -

dom The Con -sti -tu -tion of the U - nit -ed States

says _____ that we're due free-dom, free dom, free dom, free dom

LEAD	CHOIR
I've got a job	I've got a job
And I want you to know	You've got a job
All of God's children	All of God's children
Surely	Surely got a job
We've got a job	We've got a job to do

We can't get freedom 'til we get through
Carrying' the cross of our Lord.

| Talk to Bull Conner... | I've got a job |
| etc.... | etc.... |

| Talk to Mr. Wallace... | I've got a job... |
| etc... | etc... |

We are fighting for	Freedom
Come on, you might not hear us	Freedom
One time for Bull Conner	Freedom
One time for Mayor Boutwell	Freedom
One time for Gov. Wallace	Freedom
One time for the city jail	Freedom
One time for the city hall	Freedom

The Consitution of the United States, says
That we're due freedom freedom
       freedom freedom (8x)
       justice justice (4x)
       yes, Lord yes, Lord (4x)
       freedom freedom (4x)
We've got a job We've got a job to do
We can't get freedom 'til we get through
Carrying the cross of our Lord.

"St. Augustine was the South's last great demonstration campaign against legally supported segregation of public accommodations, the struggle continuing right up to signing of the civil rights law, as though to illustrate daily the desperate need for the law."

Pat Watters, New South

We're Gonna March In St. Augustine Tonight, My Lord

Adaption of spiritual - SCLC

"This was about the roughest city we've had -- forty-five straight nights of beatings and intimidation. In church every night we'd see people sitting there with bandages on. Some would sit with shotguns between their legs. We marched regularly at night. We kept being ordered not to march especially at night because it was so dangerous. We sang every night before we went out to get up our courage. The Klan was always waiting for us -- these folk with the chains and bricks and things -- Hoss Manucy and his gang. After we were attacked we'd come back to the church, and somehow always we'd come back bleeding, singing 'I love everybody.., 'It was hard. "

Dorothy Cotton - SCLC

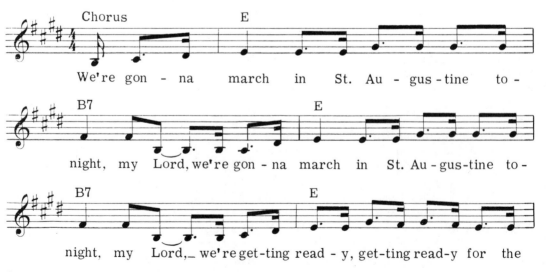

free-dom — day, my Lord, — my Lord. — Are you
read - y for your free-dom? Oh, yes. — Are you
read - y for the jour - ney? — Oh yes. — Do you
want your free - dom? — Oh yes. — We're gon - na
march in St. Au - gus-tine to - night, my Lord. —

CHORUS
We're gonna march in St. Augustine tonight, my Lord,
We're gonna march in St. Augustine tonight, my Lord,
We're getting ready, getting ready for the freedom day,
My Lord, my Lord.

Are you ready for your freedom?   Oh yes
Are you ready for the journey?   Oh yes
Do you want your freedom?   Oh yes
We're gonna march in St. Augustine tonight, my Lord.

CHORUS
We're gonna march... etc.

Are you ready, my sister?   Oh yes
Are you ready for the journey?   Oh yes
Do you want your freedom?   Oh yes
We're gonna march in St. Augustine tonight, my Lord.

"On two of St. Augustine's murky nights, after state troopers in large numbers had been called in against beatings, brick and acid throwing and other violence against non-violent demonstrations, white people bearing anti-Negro signs, led by racists, marched in a demonstration procession of their own through the main Negro neighborhood of the city. The troopers, in a line longer than the procession of 170, walked beside them to protect them, as they had also done for the Negroes. The white marchers included persons recognizable as members of the mob which had waited nightly to shout at and attack the Negro demonstrators. There were also children and women. Two boys, the age for Boy Scout hikes, shambled along, side by side, eyes excited.

When this strange procession, with the armed troopers flashing lights to both sides, their police dogs barking, reached the entrance to the Negro neighborhood, a sign greeted them: 'Welcome. Peace and brotherhood to you.'

On the second night, when the procession filed into the same street, it was lined on both sides by Negroes. Some held signs: 'I am an American'... 'Equality for all in '64'... They extended the length of the street, a good three blocks, outnumbering the white marchers probably three to one. They were still, almost motionless. And as the procession of whites, with Confederate flags and big American flag, and their own signs -- 'Kill the Civil Rights Bill'.. 'Put George Wallace on the Supreme Court' ... 'Don't Tread on Me' ... went by, the Negroes sang their song: 'I Love Everybody'.

Slowly, mournfully, softly, along the whole street, as the silent procession went by, they sang. An old Negro man and woman stood, arm in arm, staring at the white procession with eyes of loathing pain. 'I love everybody in my heart'... they sang. A second floor porch over a store was filled with Negroes, staring down, singing. 'Look up that nigger's dress,' one in the march said. Others shushed him. The song continued:

' I love everybody, I love everybody, I love everybody in my heart...You can't make me doubt Him, you can't make me doubt Him, You can't make me doubt Him in my heart.' "

Pat Watters, New South

I Love Everybody

Adaption of spiritual - SCLC

I love everybody, I love everybody,
  I love everybody in my heart,
You can't make me doubt Him,
  You can't make me doubt Him,
  You can't make me doubt Him in my heart.
The Klan can't make me doubt Him...

I feel the fire burning....

I know freedom is a-comin'...

I love Hoss Manucy...

"Then somebody would always stop, because it was hard to sing 'I love Hoss Manucy' when he'd just beat us up, to say a little bit about what love really was. He's still a person with some degree of dignity in the sight of God, and we don't have to like him, but we have to love him. He's been damaged too. So we sing it, and the more we sing it, the more we grow in ability to love people who mistreat us so bad."

Dorothy Cotton - SCLC

Wade In The Water

Traditional spiritual

"I remember the wade-ins because the bump hasn't gone off my jaw yet. We had taken a lot of kids down to the beach, not really realizing it was gonna be so bad. As I approached the water I could see it was tense -- all these policemen congregated there there and five or six feet away a group of hoodlums. They started yelling obscenities at us, but we went on -- myself and a group of teen-age girls. We were afraid but we felt we just had to go on.

We stood at the edge of the water for awhile and it was quiet -- an awful kind of quiet. Then two or three of the fellows would run and charge the group -- not hitting or anything, but just running into the group. The girls would just step aside. I thought they would leave us alone, so I encouraged the girls to go ahead and swim. Some fellows who were working with the movement, larger fellows, were out there; but somehow they picked on the group of girls.

Finally they really charged. It was obvious they felt they just couldn't take it anymore -- our being there. They knocked those little girls like they were men. One girl got a broken nose, and there were messed up eyes and faces.

There was a white fellow back on the beach saying to the policemen, 'you're supposed to protect them. Why don't you protect them?' And it was so obvious that they weren't there to protect us, but that they were friends of the hoodlums.

After the beating we went away. We sang, "Wade in the Water' and decided to go back another day."

Dorothy Cotton - SCLC

Chorus

Wade in the wa - ter, wade in the

28

wa - ter, chil - dren, wade in the wa - ter,

Verse

God's gon - na trou - ble — the wa - ter. Well

Jor - dan Riv - er is chill - y and cold, —

God's gon - na trou - ble — the wa - ter, Well it

chills my bod - y but not my soul, —

God's gon - na trou - ble the wa - ter.

Wade in the water, wade in the water, children,
Wade in the water, God's gonna trouble the water.

Jordan River is chilly and cold, God's gonna trouble the water.
It chills my body, but not my soul, God's gonna trouble the water.

Tell me who's that comin' all dressed in white...
Well it looks like children fighting for their rights...

Tell me who's that coming all dressed in red...
Well it looks like children Martin Luther King led...

Wade in the water...

Danville, Virginia, erupted into racial turmoil in late May, 1963, and ran a close race with Birmingham for top honors in police brutality. The issues were segregated public facilities, discrimination in employment, schools which were integrated in a token manner, and poor conditions generally in the Negro neighborhoods.

There were marches of protest almost every day from May 31 to June 5, culminating finally in the demonstrators being rushed and brutally beaten by policemen.

Legend Of Danville

Words & Music: Matthew Jones

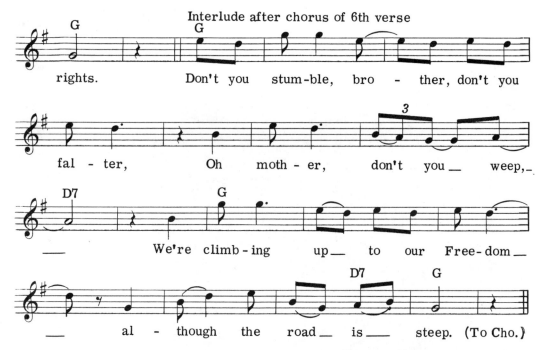

Interlude after chorus of 6th verse

rights. Don't you stum-ble, bro - ther, don't you fal - ter, Oh moth - er, don't you ___ weep, ___ ___ We're climb - ing up ___ to our Free-dom ___ ___ al - though the road ___ is ___ steep. (To Cho.)

In Danville on June the tenth
In the year of sixty-three,
From Bibleway Church to the court-
house
Some people marched to be free.

CHORUS: (after each verse)
Move on, move on, move on with the
freedom fight.
Move on, move on, we're fighting for
equal rights.

The night was dark and the journey
long
As they marched two abreast
But with the spirit of freedom's song
They didn't need no rest.

As they fell down on their knees
Led by Reverend McGhee
He looked up and cried, 'Lord,
please
We want to be free. '

They heard the voice of Chief
McCann
As it cut across the prayer,
I'll never forget those violent words,
'Nigger, get out of here!'

And as they heard those brutal words
They didn't turn around
And the water from the fire hose
Knocked them to the ground.

And as they fell down on the ground
They were hit with the billy sticks
I'll never forget that terrible sound
As the people's heads did split.

CHORUS, and interlude:
Don't you stumble brother, don't you
falter,
Oh mother, don't you weep,
We're climbing up to our freedom
Although the road is steep.

On June 13th we marched again
They used the tear gas bombs
The grand jury indicted us
On five thousand dollar bond.

In Danville town's corrupted courts
We got no justice done.
We were found guilty before the trial
And the judge he wore a gun.

Demonstrating G.I.

Words & Music: Matthew Jones

"On July 11, 1963, there was a soldier boy that came home to Danville. He saw what was going on and he had on his uniform. The Secretary of Defense issued a statement: 'You can go overseas and fight in a uniform, but you can't come back over here picketing and demonstrating in your uniform. That's un-American.'

So he got up at a mass meeting and said, 'I'm an American fighting man. I'm gonna defend my country as long as I can, and if I can defend my country overseas, why don't you set my people free?'"

Matthew Jones - SNCC

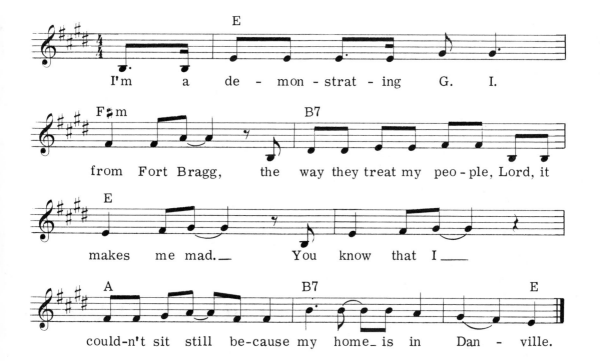

I'm a de - mon - strat - ing G. I.

from Fort Bragg, the way they treat my peo - ple, Lord, it

makes me mad. _ You know that I __

could-n't sit still be-cause my home_ is in Dan - ville.

CHORUS: (repeat after each verse)
I'm a demonstrating G. I. from Fort
  Bragg
And the way they treat my people, Lord,
  it makes me mad.
You know that I couldn't sit still
Because my home is in Danville.

I came home one Friday night,
I saw my sister fighting for her rights
I said, "Keep on Sis, and I'll be back
Standing tall in my boots so black. "

Sitting in camp I read the paper
I said to my sargeant, "I'll see you
  later, "
I caught the bus and came on home
"I told you Sis, you wouldn't be alone. "

I got arrested on Sunday ever,
The policeman said, "You've been
  overseas,
But don't you forget one simple fact,
That your skin is still black. "

I was bound in jail for over a week
All I got was some beans to eat,
On a rusty tray, I was fed
And I slept on an iron bed.

Secretary of Defense, MacNamara
Said, "Come on Boy, what's the
  matter?
I don't care if you fight for freedom
But please take off your uniform. "

I said, "Well I'm an American
  fighting man,
And I'll defend my country as long
  as I can,
But if I can defend it overseas,
Why can't you set my people free?"

Come on army, air force and navy,
Come on you soldiers, and don't be lazy,
If you want to integrate,
Come on down here and demonstrate.

Atlanta, Georgia, proclaims itself "a city too busy to hate." Still the Civil Rights organizations with headquarters there are working to force the city beyond tokenism.

Oginga Odinga

Words & Music: Matthew Jones

"Back on December 21, 1963, the State Department decided they were gonna send a Kenyan Diplomat named Oginga Odinga on an integrated tour of Atlanta, Georgia. Now we all know Atlanta, Georgia, is not integrated. So when they were planning his tour, they kinda bypassed the SNCC office, 'cause they know we're gonna show him exactly where it is ... we're gonna show him where the ghettoes are, tell him about the schools in three shifts and all this kinda thing. So since they wouldn't bring Mr. Oginga Odinga to us, we went to Mr. Oginga Odinga. We took some freedom records and some song books up to the Peachtree Manor -- that's one of the integrated hotels in Atlanta -- it ain't but about two! And we were able to bring the word of freedom to Mr. Oginga Odinga. And we sang 'We Shall Overcome'. And Mr. Odinga then said the Swahili word for freedom, Uhuru!

It's a funny thing about that word freedom. It doesn't make any difference if its Swahili, Japanese, Chinese, English or French, it's got that certain ring to it. So we just marched right out of the Peachtree Manor and over to the peacefully segregated Toddle House that was next door. And we sat in. The waitress had the nerve to tell us, 'Sorry, but we don't serve colored people here.' Now, what did she want to say that for? We just sat right down.

We sort of thank Mr. Odinga for revitalizing the movement in Atlanta. From this incident, we wrote a song which we call Oginga Odinga. "

Matthew Jones - SNCC

34

Verse

We went down to the Peach-tree Ma-nor to see O - gin - ga O - din - ga. The po-lice say "What's the mat - ter" to see O - gin - ga O - din - ga. The po-lice he look might-y hard at O - gin - ga O - din - ga. He got scared 'cause he was an ex - Mau - Mau, to see O - gin - ga O - din - ga.

Chorus

O - gin -ga O-din - ga, O - gin -ga O-din - ga, O - gin - ga O-din - ga of Ken - ya. *(who)* O -

Following verses sung to first two lines of verse melody.

We went down to the Peachtree Manor to see Oginga Odinga.
The police say, 'what's the matter?' to see Oginga Odinga.
The police he look mighty hard at Oginga Odinga
He got scared 'cause he was an ex-Mau-Mau, to see Oginga Odinga.

CHORUS:
Oginga, Odinga, Oginga Odinga, Oginga Odinga, of Kenya, who?
Oginga Odinga, Oginga Odinga, Oginga Odinga of Kenya,
Uh-hu-hu-hu-ru   haaa!
Uh-hu-hu-hu-ru   haaa!
Freedom now..ow..oww,   haaa!
Freedom now..ow..oww,   haaa!

Oginga say 'look-a here, what's going on down in Selma?
If you white folks don't straighten up, I'm gonna call Jomo Kenyatta!'

CHORUS

The white folks down in Mississippi will knock you on your rump.
And if you holler Freedom, you'll wind up in the swamp!

CHORUS

The Prophecy
Of A SNCC Field Secretary

Words & Music: Matthew Jones

"Around the year 1990, I don't like to be a fortune-teller, but I hope we have a little freedom by then. And most of us here will be grandparents by then. Your grandchildren will ask you what you did back in the 1960s. Now we don't want you telling no lies. Don't be saying, 'I led the demonstrations in Birmingham,' when you know you didn't do a thing ... probably sitting up in New York the whole time.

So we have a song called 'The Prophecy of a SNCC Field Secretary.' This grandfather is sitting back telling his grandchildren what he did."

Matthew Jones, speaking at a SNCC conference

Come here child, sit on my knee, let me tell you how we got free, It all start-ed a

long time a-go___ in nine-teen six-

ty. T'was the Stu-dent Non-vio-lent Co-

or-din-at-ing Com-mit-tee, The Stu-dent Non-

vio-lent Co-or-din-at-ing Com-mit-tee.

Hum behind narration

mm ___

SPOKEN

What happened in 1960, Grandpa? How we got free?

Come here, child, and let me tell you how we all got free,
It all happened a long time ago, in 1960.

CHORUS

It was the Student Nonviolent Coordinating Committee,
The Student Nonviolent Coordinating Committee.

How'd it all get started, Grandpa?
You mean to tell me after I got all these schools
integrated, you're gonna ask me that? I should
be asking you.
But I don't know, grandpa.
Well, I'll tell you then.

It all started in North Carolina, the city of Greensboro,
When some students at A & T decided to stop the white man's terror.

Grandpa, what's all this terror?
Well, let me think...

Segregation was the terror, the students fought this sin,
They used a powerful weapon they called the sit-in.

> You know whose white folks really got scared.
> What were they scared of, Grandpa?
> They really got scared of...

The Student Nonviolent Coordinating Committee... etc.

> What were some of their names, Grandpa?
> Their names? You mean outside of me?
> Yeah, grandpa.
> Well, ah... John Lewis, they said he did all the
> work, he was the Chairman. But really I was the
> chairman underneath, you know how it is.
> There was Charles Sherrod...

I remember a long time ago when things were mighty hard.
Up popped a nonviolent man, his name was Charles Sherrod, of

The Student Nonviolent Coordinating Committee... etc.

> You know, I'm trying to think of who the Exec-
> utive Secretary was... Never seem to remember
> that fellow's name...

> I thought you told me <u>you</u> were the chairman,
> Grandpa?
> I told you I was the chairman underneath. You
> know you always have someone underneath doing all
> the work. I didn't make the history books be-
> cause I believe in sharing. I'm trying to think
> of his name...

> You mean you were the 'undercover Uncle Tom...'

> You know this younger generation is going wild.
> We wanted integration, we didn't want you to
> be a <u>dis</u>-grace. Let me see if I can think of
> his name...

Freedom, freedom... it's a shame, I can't remember his name,
Freedom, his name was Jim Forman, of

The Student Nonviolent Coordinating Committee... etc.

"In February, 1964, freedom workers were picketing Leb's restaurant in Atlanta. Thousands of passers-by, diners-out, and spectators crowded the four corners of the intersection. Demonstrators lined the two sides of the street. Suddenly an old man dressed in the red-piped, white satin robes of a Klan Cyclops limped through the narrow aisle of the sidewalk between restaurant and curb, leading a line of white-sheeted followers and a half dozen shirt-sleeved boys and men.

"Reporters, police, and spectators watched pop-eyed with apprehension as the white line moved valiant and stony-faced through the two dense, predominantly black walls of demonstrators. The Negro youngsters, after a loaded pause, sang 'We Shall Overcome.'

"The second or third time through, several Klansmen called out their slogans against the rising assault of music:
<blockquote>
'I'm a white man and proud of it!'
'Niggers, go home!'
'Kill the niggers!'
</blockquote>

"'Black and white together, black and white together...' sang the laughing Negroes, most of them now dancing as they clapped. The music swelled and pounded louder, faster, and more aggressive, and the twisting girls and laughing boys danced and clapped closer and closer to the Klan.

"The young voices sang at the angry white faces, 'we shall brothers be...we shall brothers be...we shall brothers be, someday...' Another line of Klansmen crossing the street was infiltrated. Several Negro boys had borrowed white table cloths from Leb's, draped them over their dark heads, and slipped into the white line to march grinning with the Klansmen.

"The singing went on for hours, until many of us thought the poor Klansmen would, indeed, be overcome by the volume of the music, the power of the beat, and the hilarity of the ridicule."

Margaret Long, "Let Freedom Sing"
The Progressive, November 1965

"On other days, when the Klan wasn't 'integrating' the line in front of Leb's they would picket down the street at Herron's, a restaurant which served black and white. On one of those days I was running back and forth taking photos of both groups when, halfway between the two, I suddenly spotted this little girl walking along with her message written on a paper napkin.'

Ken Thompson, photographer
National Council of Churches

AMERICUS

When demonstrations began in Americus, young people were arrested by the hundreds. When the city jail was full, they were transported to stockades about a mile out of town.

"The boys went around front and kept the guard busy by talking to him. I crawled around the back and shot pictures through the bars in the rear. All the girls had been arrested in demonstrations in Americus. Some had been in the stockade a few days, others had been there for three weeks; they had no furniture, blankets or clothing other than what they had been arrested in. The toilet was clogged and gave off a smell strong enough to be sickening outside the building. The only source of water for washing or drinking was a dripping shower head. Their daily food consisted of four cold hamburgers each in the morning. When I saw them they were in good spirits."

Danny Lyon, SNCC photographer

You Should Have Been There

Adaption of spiritual by
Virginia Davis & Amanda Bowens

I   said   you,   you,   you   should-a   been   there,

You, you, you should-a been there I said you, you, you should-a been there to __ roll, free-dom, roll.__ Come on and roll, roll free-dom, roll, roll free-dom, roll, roll free-dom, roll, roll free-dom, I want to get my free-dom be-fore I die, roll, free-dom roll. __

I say you, you, you should-a been there,
You, you, you should-a been there,
I said you, you, you should have been there
To roll, freedom, roll.

LEAD	GROUP
Come on and roll	roll freedom
Roll	roll freedom
Roll	roll freedom
Roll	roll freedom
I want to get my freedom, before I die	
Roll, freedom, roll.	

I said, Wallace, you should have been there,
Wallace... etc.

I said, Lyndon, you should have been there,
Lyndon... etc.

I Ain't Scared A' Your Jail

Words - SNCC and SCLC

"You know for so long the white man in the South used the jails to scare Negroes. They've lynched a lot of Negroes and there have been many, many cases where Negroes have been killed and their bodies mutilated, and nothing has been done about it. The Federal Government has refused to do anything. If you go to the court house and try to register they tell you,

'If you live on my plantation, I'm gonna get you thrown off. And I'm gonna get the sheriff to throw you in jail and throw the key away.'

But in Mississippi we had a Freedom Day. One lady brought her little son. He had a sign, say: I'M TOO YOUNG TO VOTE, BUT MY MOTHER WANT TO VOTE. A policeman called him over and said,

'If you don't pull off that sign and throw it away, boy, I'm gonna throw you in jail.'

The little boy remembered the song that we sing, and he looked up to the policeman and said,

'Mister, I ain't scared of your jail, 'cause I want my freedom!'"

Sam Block - SNCC

I ain't scared of your jail because I want my freedom,
I want my freedom, I want my freedom,
I ain't scared of your jail because I want my freedom,
I want my freedom now.

We'll march downtown because.... etc.

We'll go to jail because....

I served ninety days because...
        "You know in all parts of the South
they use dogs and sic 'em on people, and they use cattle prods.
Not only that, but they beat you upside the head with sticks.
They squirt water on you with a big hose. So sometimes we sing:"

I ain't scared of your dogs because...

I ain't scared of your sticks because...

I ain't scared of your hose because...
        "And sometimes they tell us, 'Well,
since you ain't scared of nothin, I'm gonna go back to the old
Southern tradition -- I'm gonna blow your brains out.' So we sing:"

I don't mind dying because....
        "And while things are going on in
Mississippi, people are doing things in other places. In Birming-
ham they sing:"
I ain't scared of no Bull* because...
We'll never turn back until....
I ain't scared of your jails because....

                                                  *Bull Conner

Nothing But A Soldier

Words and Music: Charles Sherrod

"For the first time in our history a major social movement, shaking the nation to its bones, is being led by youngsters ... To be with them, walking a picket line in the rain in Hatties-burg, or sleeping on a cot in a cramped 'office' in Greenville; to watch them walk out of the stone jailhouse in Albany; to see them jabbed by electric prod poles and flung into paddy wagons in Selma; or to link arms and sing at the close of a church meeting in the Delta -- is to feel the presence of greatness. It is a greatness that comes from their relationship to history, and it does not diminish when they are discovered to be human: to make mistakes or feel fear, to act with envy, or hostility or even violence.

All Americans owe them a debt. Theirs was the silent genera-tion until they spoke, the complacent generation until they marched and sang, the money-seeking generation until they re-nounced comfort and security to fight for justice in the dank and dangerous hamlets of the Black Belt. "

Howard Zinn, <u>SNCC: The New Abolitionists</u>

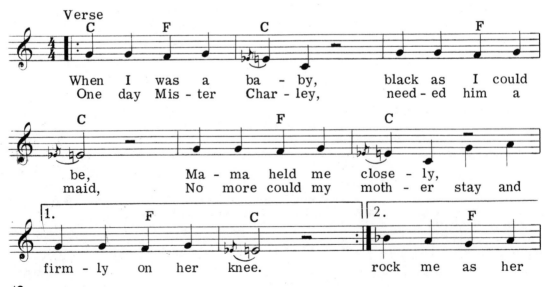

When I was a ba - by, black as I could
One day Mis - ter Char - ley, need - ed him a

be, Ma - ma held me close - ly,
maid, No more could my moth - er stay and

1. firm - ly on her knee. 2. rock me as her

When I was a baby, black as I could be
Mama held me closely, firmly on her knee.
One day Mister Charley needed him a maid
No more could my mother stay and rock me as her babe.

CHORUS: (after each verse)
Nothing but a soldier, nothing but a soldier,
Nothing but a soldier can make it in.

Daddy never knew me, never wiped my tears,
Never saw me crying, never knew my fears
Working for the white man, sun-up 'till sun-down,
Come home wet and tired, he would always wear a frown.

I became a young man, proud as I could be
Used to hear them saying, 'Hang him on a tree, '
Tree limb couldn't hold me, segregation tried,
Jumped the gun for freedom, getting closer every stride.

Folks say don't go marching without an alibi,
But I say give me freedom before the day I die,
We don't need the H-bomb, rockets do not serve,
We have got non-violence, packs more power for every nerve.

Hoses were a-spurting, police everywhere,
Dragged me to the wagon, stripped to underwear,
Dogs tore off my clothing, cow prods burnt my flesh,
Cops beat me with blackjacks, they were stomping on my chest.

Blood ran down my forehead, blood ran down my back,
Threw me in the jailhouse, face down on the rock,
Told Judge Jim Crow slowly, I may not be brave,
You can jail my body, but I'll never be your slave.

Most of the publicity in the South is given to the big demonstrations when they reach a crisis stage. A quieter operation, which rarely receives notice, is also at work. In 1962, the Southern Christian Leadership Conference took over the Highlander Experiment in Basic Education -- the Citizenship School. Under the direction of Mrs. Septima Clark, the citizenship school idea has spread across the South.

More than 1,400 persons have received one week of intensified training in adult literacy methods and basic understanding of politics, and have returned to eleven southern states to share their newly acquired knowledge with their neighbors.

According to SCLC, ''the curriculum has changed from the basic reading and writing program to one including: Simple Banking, Consumer Economics, The Importance of the Precinct Meeting, Implementation of the Civil Rights Bill, Negro History, Planned Parenthood, and Federally Assisted Programs. The change is in keeping with new problems as they appear in the various areas of the South.

In 1964 the work paid off in big numbers. The November 3rd election saw Negroes from remote rural areas standing in line early in the morning waiting to cast a ballot for the first time in their lives. This happened all across the South. It showed the courage that had been instilled in these people who earlier feared jailings, beatings, and other reprisals. They also knew why they needed to vote.''

SCLC newsletter

Go Ahead

Traditional spiritual adapted by
citizenship school ladies from South Carolina

Go a - head, and go a - head, There is
some - thing tell - ing me to go a - head.

LEAD	GROUP
Go ahead	go ahead
Go ahead	go ahead
Something's telling me go ahead	
Go ahead	go ahead
Go ahead	go ahead
There's something telling me go ahead.	
Pray a prayer	Pray a prayer
And go ahead	go ahead
Something's telling me... etc.	
Sing a song	sing a song
And go ahead... etc.	
Cast your vote	cast your vote
And go ahead... etc.	

Up Above My Head

Adaption of gospel song by Betty Mae Fikes

This is an upbeat gospel version of the old spiritual "Over My Head." Betty Mae Fikes of Selma, Alabama, adapted it and introduced it at a Sing for Freedom Conference in Atlanta in 1964 -- a gathering of freedom singers and song-leaders from across the South.

lieve   there's   a   God___   some - where.___

LEAD	GROUP
Up above my head	Up above my head
I see freedom in the air	I see freedom in the air
Up above my head	Up above my head
I see freedom in the air	I see freedom in the air
Up above my head	Up above my head
I see freedom in the air	I see freedom in the air

And I really do believe, I said I really do believe,
        There's a God somewhere.

Up above my head, I hear praying in the air...etc.

Up above my head, I hear singing in the air...

Up above my head, I hear music in the air...

If my mother won't go, I'm gonna go anyhow...

If you can't go, let your children go...

If my brother can't go, don't let him hinder me...

Up above my head, I see freedom in the air...

FREEDOM IS
A CONSTANT STRUGGLE

The Mississippi Project

Why Was The Darkie Born?

Traditional - Adaptions
by James Bevel & Bernice Reagon

James Bevel heard an old man sing this song in Mississippi.
He asked where it came from, but the old man didn't know.

Mom - my, __ why was the dark - ie __ born?

Mom - my, __ why was the dark - ie __ born?

Some - bod - y had to pick __ the __ cot - ton,

some-bod - y had to pull __ the __ corn, Some-bod - y had to

build a great __ na - tion, and that's why the dark - ie was a-

born, that's why the dark - ie was __ born.

Mommy, why was the Darkie born?
Mommy, why was the Darkie born?
Somebody had to pick the cotton,
Somebody had to pull the corn,
Somebody had to build a great nation,
That's why the Darkie was born.
That's why the Darkie was born.

Mommy, why was the Darkie born? (2x)
Somebody had to cry at midnight,
Somebody had to weep and moan,
Somebody had to love everybody,
That's why the Darkie was born (2x)

Mommy...
Somebody had to beat the drums
Somebody had to blow the horn
Somebody had to sing the blues
That's....

Mommy....
Somebody had to go to jail,
Somebody had to walk a picket line,
Somebody had to fight for freedom,
That's...

"My feeling about the song in that the Darkie was created by white people. A group of people were brought over from Africa and everything that made them what they were was stripped from them. They made a Negro -- a colored man -- a Darkie. The question is why? Why was it necessary to have a Darkie? Why couldn't we have retained the word African, as the Italian people are still Italians and the Spanish people are still Spanish? Why was it necessary for the white man to make a new person -- a Darkie?"

Bernice Reagon - SNCC

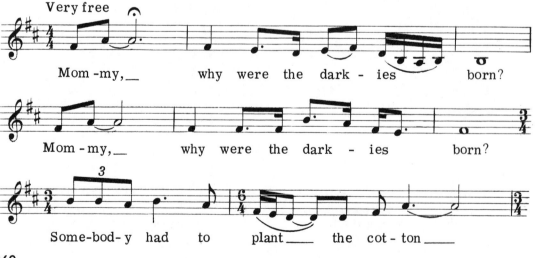

Very free

Mom -my,__ why were the dark - ies born?

Mom -my,__ why were the dark - ies born?

Some-bod-y had to plant__ the cot-ton__

Some-bod-y had to pull the corn, Some-bod-y had to work __ for noth-in' __ That's why the dark-ies were __ born.

Verse-Very free

(4) Oh, Lord, __ I __ am try - in' work-in' hard __ un - til the day, When __ my ba - by won't have __ to wor - ry __ 'bout be - in' born black this way. _____

Mommy...
Somebody had to cry at midnight
Somebody had to weep and moan
Somebody had to sing the blues, child,
That's....

Oh Lord, I'm trying
Working hard until the day
When my baby won't have to worry
'Bout being born black this way.

Mommy....
Somebody had to plant the cotton,
Somebody had to pull the corn,
Somebody had to build this nation,
That's why.....

Mommy, why were the Darkies born?
Mommy, why were the Darkies born?
Somebody had to plant the cotton,
Somebody had to pull the corn,
Somebody had to work for nothin',
That's why the Darkies were born.

Come here my little baby,
Sit on your mama's knee
And I will try to tell you
Why your Ma ain't free.

Freedom Train A' Comin'

Adaption of union song

Hear__ that - a free - dom train a -
com - ing, com - ing, com - ing, Hear that free - dom train a -
com - ing, com - ing, com - ing, Hear that free - dom train a -
com-ing, com-ing, com-ing, Get on board, oh,__ oh get on board.

Hear that Freedom Train a' comin', comin', comin'
Hear that Freedom Train a' comin', comin', comin'
Hear that Freedom Train a' comin', comin', comin'
Get on board, get on board.

It'll be carryin' nothing but freedom, freedom, freedom (3x)
Get on board, get on board.

They'll be comin' by the thousand, thousand, thousand (3x)
Get on board, get on board.

It'll be carryin' freedom fighters, fighters, fighters, (3x)
Get on board, get on board.

It'll be carryin' registered voters, voters, voters (3x)
Get on board, get on board.

It'll be rollin' through Mississippi, Mississippi (3x)
Get on board, get on board.

Hear that Freedom Train a' comin'....

"It's no use of you being worried, trying to turn back. It's no use of you saying 'I'm not in this mess!' because if you were born with your skin black, you were automatically born in the mess. So you just might as well come on and get on the Freedom Train. Get on board, children, get on board."

Sam Block, SNCC

THE SUMMER PROJECT

"The 1964 Mississippi Summer Project was an operation like nothing in the nation's history. Seven hundred college students from all over the country showed up at Oxford, Ohio, for an orientation session organized by the National Council of Churches. There, young veterans of the Black Belt tried to give them realistic pictures of the dangers they faced. They were taught how to protect themselves from injury without responding violently. They talked passionately about their own fears, their indecision, their dreams. Then they climbed into buses and cars and headed South.

"The volunteers were mostly white, northern, middle-class. The staff people -- mainly SNCC, some CORE, a few SCLC --were generally Negro, Southern, sent by lower-class parents to Negro colleges, from which they darted off into the movement. Together, in clusters, they fanned out across Mississippi.

"Besides the students there were several hundred Northern professional people-- doctors, nurses, lawyers, ministers, teachers. The doctors and nurses were part of a new phenomenon which seemed to grow up overnight, called the Medical Committee for Human Rights. The lawyers formed an efficient corps such as had never been seen before in the civil rights troubles of this decade. As for the ministers, they were everywhere: on picket lines, in Freedom Houses, at mass meetings.

"The Mississippi Summer had an effect impossible to calculate..."

Howard Zinn, SNCC, The New Abolitionists

"The most devastating affront to the old order in Mississippi and the most momentous challenge to the prevailing caste system, has been the fact of nearly a thousand white summer visitors living and working amiably with Negro families."

James Silver, Foreword to Letters from Mississippi

64

"Man like I don't even believe what I just did. You really had to be here to appreciate it. I took a bath. But no ordinary bath 'cause there's no running water. No, we take this bucket out in the back yard and fill it with water warmed over a fire. It's pitch black so we shine Mr. Clark's truck lights on the bucket. Then I strip down naked and stand in the bucket wash. That is the way you take a bath around here."

Letters from Mississippi

"Everyday this week the men of the community hammered and poured cement. At noon, about seven or eight women all gathered at the center with fried chicken, fish, salad, gallons of cool-aid and apple turnovers, and served them to the men, we teachers, and each other. It is a thing of beauty to see us all work together. Tuesday and Wednesday was the laying of the sub-floor. Two men cut the wood, two or three teenage boys and girls laid the wood down and hammered it in, a few more are bringing more wood. It should be up by Saturday.

"The land was given by a local man for 'the sum of one dollar', and deeds were drawn up. The teenagers are selling refreshments to raise money for the center, as well as membership cards for a dollar. It will hold the library, a snack-bar office space and recreation area...

"The men (and some of us when we have time) work on the building up to ten hours a day with a 100 degree sun beating down and the humidity so high one's clothing becomes soaking wet after only a few minutes work. The building is guarded at night because these people, after having had their homes shot into and having a couple of crosses burned in the middle of their community during the last few months, do not intend to have all their hard work go up in flames right away..."

Letters from Mississippi

"The major contribution of the Mississippi Summer Project were the 'freedom schools'.

"The object of the Freedom School was not to cram a prescribed amount of factual material into young minds, but to give them that first look into new worlds which would, some day if not immediately, lead them to books and people and ideas not found in the everyday lives of Mississippi Negroes."

Howard Zinn, <u>SNCC, The New Abolishionists</u>

Another major portion of the summer went to canvassing and registering voters for the Mississippi Freedom Democratic Party.

"Yesterday we canvassed...One lady couldn't work because she had cut her leg badly with the hoe while chopping cotton, and her leg was full of stitches. She lived in a two-room unpainted shack (kindly provided by the management). You climbed on the porch by stepping on a bucket -- there were huge holes in the porch for the unwary. The woman was sitting dejectedly on the bed as she couldn't walk very well. She was surrounded by shy children, some of them naked. We tried to explain what Freedom Registration meant -- it seemed like a rather abstract approach to her problems..."

Letters from Mississippi

"Dear Mom,

"I have become so close to the family I am staying with -- eleven people -- that Mrs. H. finally paid me a great compliment. She was introducing me to one of her Negro women friends and said, 'This is Nancy, my adopted daughter!'

"All evening I have little children crawling over me and big boys, 16, my buddies, combing my hair, confiding in me, appreciating me, because I will open my heart and mind to them and listen and care for them and show my concern. I may be sex- and love-starved, as some like to picture me, but at least I have faced the problem and have found my own inner peace by being with people who have not forgotten how to love.

"Really, to tell the honest truth, I am just a little bit tired of hearing you and others, and for a long time even myself, think, worry, discuss, write and talk about all the deep down psychological reasons for your personal problems. When I see these simple people living lives of relative inner peace, love, honor, courage, and humor, I lose patience with people who sit and ponder their belly buttons..."

Letters from Mississippi

"The Mississippi Caravan of Music was a cultural arm of the Summer Project. Singing is the backbone and balm of this movement. Somehow you can go on in the face of violence and death, cynicism and inaction of the FBI, the indifference of the Federal Government when you can sing with your band of brothers.

"Those Caravan singers who could stay for a period longer than a week, spent two or more days at each project. Others went from place to place on a rather hectic schedule. A typical Caravan day would begin with the singers participating in a class on Negro history at the Freedom School. They showed that freedom songs were sung back in the days of slavery -- how some songs even blueprinted the way to freedom on the underground railroad. The singers demonstrated the important contribution of Negro music in every aspect of American musical and cultural history. For children who have been brainwashed by the public school system to accept the myth of their own inferiority, this was an exhilarating revelation. For the majority of adults as well as children it was the first time they had heard of such great musical artists as Leadbelly and Big Bill Broonzy. For many, the music they had learned to be ashamed of was given new stature by the visiting musicians.

"Completing a program at one Freedom School the Caravan group would travel on to another. There they would hold a workshop informally with the students in the afternoon. After time out for dinner there would be a mass rally or a hootenanny that might last three hours. It seemed to me that the farther out in the country and the more ramshackle the wooden church, the greater was the singing.

"Always the singers would return to Freedom House late at night and sing on into the early hours of the morning with the civil rights workers who had little other opportunity to just relax and let off steam.

"Sometimes Caravan Activities stimulated local white people to participate for the first time in an integrated function (non-violently that is!). A number of white Mississippians turned out for concerts that Julius Lester, Len Chandler and Cordell Reagon gave on the Gulf Coast. When Pete Seeger sang in McComb, two white college students came to hear him. Several days later they had dinner with some of the civil rights workers. Soon afterward, when Pete sang in Jackson, four students from Ole Miss attended. They, too, were so impressed that they showed up a few days later in the Jackson COFO office, expressing interest in the Freedom Schools. All of this took considerable courage on the part of these local white youths."

Bob Cohen, director
Mississippi Caravan of Music

71

Father's Grave

Words and Music: Len Chandler, Jr.
© 1964, Fall River Music

Len and Cordell Reagon travelled together during the summer Caravan through Mississippi and other areas of the South. They visited the house where Cordell grew up in Waverly, Tennessee. Cordell had talked often about not getting to his father's funeral on time. They went to the graveyard and cut the weeds down over the grave. They talked about freedom and about whether their children would have to go through the difficult changes they were going through in the next generation.

This is a personal song, yet its chorus speaks for many in the movement.

al - ways been a - lone And of that weed - y___ grave that___ held_____ my clos - est kin._____ And as I cut the weeds from o'er my fa - ther's grave, fa-ther's grave, I _____ swore no child I bore would be ___ a slave.

With my swing blade in my hand, as I looked across the land
And thought of all the places that I'd been,
Of that old house that I called home,
Where I'd always been alone
And of that weedy grave that held my closest kin.

CHORUS: (after each verse)
And as I cut the weeds from o'er my father's grave, father's grave,
I swore no child I bore would be a slave.

Oh, the old house was a shell, there were weeds around the well,
And I touched the rusty hinge that held no door
And the roof was caving in, It was always sort of thin,
And I found the place where the ash pan burned the floor.

I thought of all the glad and the good times that I had
With my pockets full of purple plums each fall
When the yard was wide and clean and the grass was short & green
Now the underbrush has laid its claim to all.

It made me feel so bad, lost the best friend that I had
And I didn't get to hear the preacher pray
Yes, and I was only eight, no, I can't recall the date
Nor the reason I was late, but a funeral just can't wait
And when I got to church they were rolling him away.

In Rosedale, Mississippi
there is one white doctor

And this doctor doesn't come
whenever peoples call

This doctor comes
later on.

But in Rosedale see
there isn't any place
For the
peoples

A Whole Lot Of Peoples Is Strong

Mrs. Ida Mae Lawrence Rosedale, Mississippi

to assemble
and talk about
the way peoples feel.

AND WHAT THEY CAN DO
About the doctor
And the school
And being Very Hungry
ALL DAY.

Because there isn't any money
Two dollars maybe
For a whole day's work
in the fields.

That's ALL.

And if you get sick
The doctor won't come

And if you get well
You got to go back out
To the fields

But you don't have to
Pretty soon.

Pretty soon
A whole lot of peoples
Won't go.

A Whole Lot of Peoples
is Strong.

"The ones that are going into this is the young, hot niggers, not our good old Mississippi niggers. These freedom workers are low-down snakes in the weeds."

O. C. Allen, farmer in Leake County

I Want My Freedom

Tune: You are My Sunshine
Words: The Rev. Mrs. Elvira Bailey

CHORUS:
I want my freedom, I want my
    freedom,
I want to be a free, free man,
I want my freedom, I want my
    freedom
I want to be a free, free man.

The other day dear, as I was
    walking,
I read a sign 'no colored allowed'
I read that sign dear, I read it over,
And I hung my head and cried.

In this America, new things are
    happening
To make the white man finally see
That we are human, that we are equal
And that we shall, we shall be free.

In this America, new things are
    happening
To make the black man finally see
That they must fight dear, that they
    must fight dear,
If they are ever to be free.

It Isn't Nice

Words by Malvina Reynolds
Music by Reynolds & Barbara Dane
© Schroder Music Co.

This song was introduced in Mississippi by Barbara Dane and Judy Collins on their trips with the Caravan of Music. It is still widely sung there.

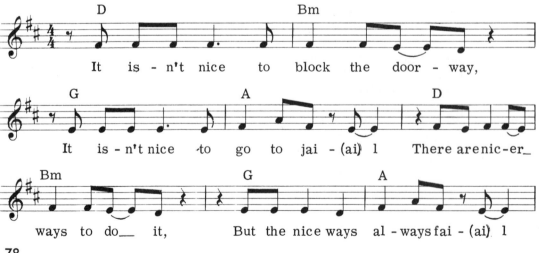

It is - n't nice to block the door - way,
It is - n't nice to go to jai - (ai) l There are nic - er
ways to do__ it, But the nice ways al - ways fai - (ai) l

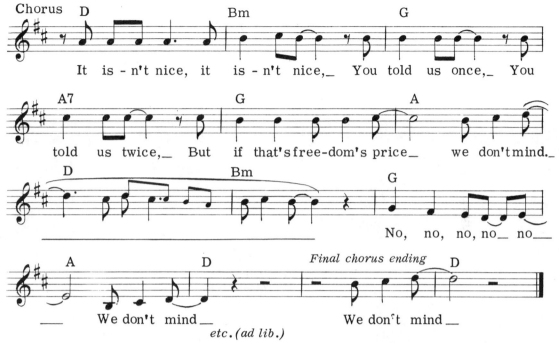

Chorus

It is-n't nice, it is-n't nice,_ You told us once,_ You told us twice,_ But if that's free-dom's price_ we don't mind._

No, no, no, no_ no_

Final chorus ending

We don't mind _ We don't mind _

etc.(ad lib.)

It isn't nice to block the doorway,
It isn't nice to go to jail,
There are nicer ways to do it
But the nice ways always fail
It isn't nice, it isn't nice
You told us once, you told us twice
But if that's freedom's price,
We don't mind.......no, no, no, no,
   no,
We don't mind.

It isn't nice to dump the groceries,
Or to sleep in on the floor,
Or to shout or cry of freedom
In the hotel or the store,
It isn't nice, it isn't nice,
You told us once, you told us twice,
But if that's freedom's price,
We don't mind...

Well, we've tried negotiations
And the token picket line,
Mister Charley didn't see us
And he might as well be blind;
When you deal with men of ice,
You can't deal with ways so nice,
But if that's freedom's price,
We don't mind...

They kidnapped boys in Mississippi,
They shot Medgar in the back,
Did you say that wasn't proper?
Did you stand out on the track?
You were quiet just like mice,
Now you say that we're not nice,
Well, if that's freedom's price,
We don't mind...

It isn't nice to block the doorway,
It isn't nice to go to jail,
There are nicer ways to do it
But the nice ways always fail
It isn't nice, it isn't nice
You told us once you told us twice,
Thanks buddy, for your advice,
Well it that's freedom's price,
We don't mind.....
WE DON'T MIND

"Never go any places where there aren't at least two roads so that people who follow you in have to watch two exits when you leave."

SNCC worker

"In this summer the stranger is the enemy, and the men of Mississippi wait and watch for him. In khaki pants and straw hat they stand their watch against the civil rights workers across the Delta counties.

"By night they ride dipping roads in the hill country to the east where that fatal plant, the kudzu vine, grows everywhere strangling grass and tree. Along Route 19 they drive through Neshoba County's scrub oak and scraggly pine forests without headlights when the moon is bright and the mist is sparse and patchy.

"For the Negroes, fear makes the night wakeful. Negro farmers check their guns and count their children as the night comes on. The short nights of summer are long -- longer than ever now because the white civil rights workers are living hidden among the Negro farm folk."

Nicholas Von Hoffman
<u>Mississippi Notebook</u>

"We are now in the midst of the 'long, hot summer' of agitation which was promised to the Innocent People of Mississippi by the savage blacks and their community masters...

"There is no racial problem here in this state. Our system of strict segregation permits the two races to live in close proximity and harmony with each other and eliminates any racial problem...

"Bi-racial groups are the greatest danger we face in this State today. We are not going to recognize the authority of any bi-racial group, NOR THE AUTHORITY OF ANY PUBLIC OFFICIAL WHO ENTERS INTO ANY AGREEMENT WITH ANY SUCH SOVIET ORGANIZATION.

"We Knights are working day and night to preserve Law and Order here in Mississippi, in the only way that it can be preserved; by strict segregation of the races, and the control of the social structure in the hands of the Christian, Anglo-Saxon White men, the only race on earth that can build and maintain just and stable governments. We are deadly serious about this business.

"Take heed, atheists and mongrels, we will not travel your path to Leninist Hall, but we will buy YOU a ticket to the Eternal if you insist. Take your choice, SEGREGATION, TRANQUILITY AND JUSTICE, OR BI-RACISM, CHAOS AND DEATH..."

The Klan Ledger
White Knights of the Ku Klux Klan
July, 1964

"The Student Nonviolent Coordinating Committee places a large order when it asks people to meet violence with non-violence. So far, here in Greenwood, they have been able to make their point -- that non-violence is tactically necessary in demonstrations. But SNCC has also, I think, encouraged self-protection, and it has proven difficult to discern where self-defense and 'defense of the community' are distinct from each other. To these young people, as to most, violence is not at all a last and regrettable, resort. To be violent has usually been, in the minds of Southerners, to be courageous. The boycott, powerful economic blow or not, does not satisfy the repressed urge of these young people to strike back.

"It is frightening to know that anything the opposition does they justify on bases of principle, and to realize that much of what they do is inspired by moral fervor. Playing on their sense of guilt is a dubious, even negligible weapon, it would seem. I saw this perverted moralism translated into violent action the other day when I was chased out of the white neighborhood with stones and curses, a car finally ran me off the road and forced me to dive into a Negro's chickencoop for safety. That little gimp-legged man with the wild blue eyes who was not a good enough shot to hit me with the rocks, who ran after me down the street with his cronies, who roared after me in his car and came up onto the dirt after me with it, who swung at me with his left hand as he went by but missed again, believed that he was striking blows for freedom, among other things -- for all that is good and right. I suppose all you can do for a man like that is pray for him. Is he wicked? If he isn't, then maybe no one is and maybe that's the proper conclusion: there are no evil men in the world, only scared ones and indignant ones and hateful ones. But if there are no evil men, there is evil; you feel it come into yourself when you view these men..."

Letters from Mississippi

82

Mississippi Goddam

Words and Music - Nina Simone
© 1964 Sam Fox Publ.

"The Summer Project headquarters in Jackson had mimeographed a list of 'incidents' from shootings to church burnings and traffic violation arrests, during the period of June 16 to August 14. It covers thirty-four pages, most of them legal size and single-spaced."

Elizabeth Sutherland, The Nation, Sept. 14, 1964

Al - a - bam - a's got me so up - set_ Ten - nes - see made me lose my rest and Ev - 'ry - bod - y knows a - bout Mis - sis - sip - pi god - dam. Can't you see it, Can't you feel it, It's all in the air,_ I can't stand the pres - sure much longer some - one_ say a prayer. Al - a - bam - a's got me so up - set,_ Ten - nes - see made me lose my rest_ and Ev - 'ry - bod - y knows a - bout Mis - sis - sip - pi god - dam._ Hound dogs_ on my trail, School chil - dren sit - ting in jail,

Alabama's got me so upset, Tennessee made me lose my rest,
And everybody knows about Mississippi goddam.
Can't you see it, can't you feel it, it's all in the air;
I can't stand the pressure much longer, someone say a prayer.
Alabama's got me so upset, Tennessee made me lose my rest,
And everybody knows about Mississippi goddam.

Hound dogs on my trail, school children sitting in jail,
Black cat cross my path, I think every day's gonna be my last.
Lord have mercy on this land of mine, we all gonna get it in due time.
Don't belong here, I don't belong there, I even stopped believing in prayer.

Don't tell me, I'll tell you, Me and my people just about due.
I've been there, so I know, they keep on saying 'Go slow.'
That's just the trouble - too slow,
Washing the windows - too slow,
Picking the cotton - too slow,
You're just plain rotten - too slow,
You're too damn lazy - too slow,
You thinkin's crazy - too slow,
Where am I going, what am I doing, I don't know. I don't know.
Just try to do your very best,
Stand up, be counted with all the rest,
'Cause everybody knows about Mississippi goddam.

Picket lines, school boycott, try to say it's a Communist plot.
All I want is equality, for my sister and brother, my people and me.
You lied to me all these years, you told me to wash & clean my ears.
Talk real fine, just dress like a lady, and you'd stop calling me Sister Sadie.
But this whole country is corrupted with lies,
You all should die and die like flies
I don't trust you any more, you keep on saying, 'Go slow.'
That's just the trouble - too slow
Desegregation - too slow
Mass participation - too slow
Unification - too slow
Do things gradually - too slow
Will bring more tragedy - too slow

Why don't you see it, why can't you feel it?
I don't know, I don't know.
You don't have to live next to me
Just give me Equality.

Everybody knows about Mississippi,
Everybody knows about Alabama,
Everybody knows about Mississippi goddam.

"Dear folks,

"Last night I was a long time before sleeping, although I was extremely tired. Every shadow, every noise -- the bark of a dog, the sound of a car -- in my fear and exhaustion was turned into a terrorist's approach. And I believed that I heard the back door open and a Klansman walk in, until he was close by the bed. Almost paralyzed by the fear, silent, I finally shone my flashlight on the spot where I thought he was standing...I tried consciously to overcome this fear. To relax, I began to breathe deep, think the words of a song, pull the sheet up close to my neck...still the tension.

"Anyone who comes down here and is not afraid I think must be crazy as well as dangerous to this project where security is quite important. But the type of fear that they mean when they, when we, sing 'we are not afraid' is the type that immobilizes...The songs help to dissipate the fear. Some of the words in the songs do not hold real meaning on their own, others become rather monotonous -- but when they are sung in unison, or sung silently by oneself, they take on new meaning beyond words or rhythm...There is almost a religious quality about some of these songs, having little to do with the usual concept of a god. It has to do with the miracle that youth has organized to fight hatred and ignorance. It has to do with the holiness of the dignity of man. The god that makes such miracles is the god I do believe in when we sing 'God is on our side.' I know I am on that god's side, and I do hope he is on ours."

Letters from Mississippi

Freedom Is A Constant Struggle

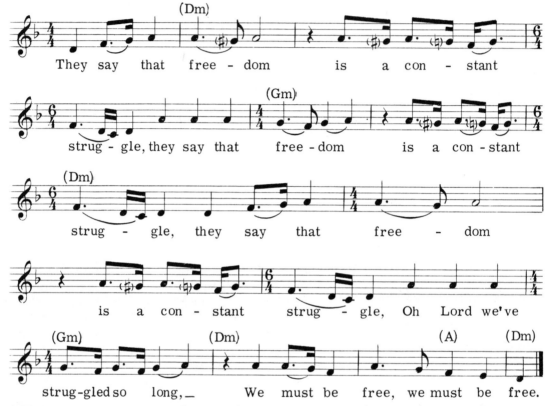

They say that freedom is a con - stant strug - gle, they say that free - dom is a con - stant strug - gle, they say that free - dom is a con - stant strug - gle, Oh Lord we've strug-gled so long, — We must be free, we must be free.

They say that freedom is a constant struggle,
They say that freedom is a constant struggle,
They say that freedom is a constant struggle,
Oh Lord, we've struggled so long,
We must be free, we must be free.

They say that freedom is a constant crying...
Oh Lord, we've cried so long....

They say that freedom is a constant sorrow....
Oh Lord, we've sorrowed so long....

They say that freedom is a constant moaning....
Oh Lord, we've moaned so long....

They say that freedom is a constant dying....
Oh Lord, we've died so long,
We must be free, we must be free.

"During gentle mid-June days in 1964, three lives converged in the campus town of Oxford, Ohio, and ended on Rock Cut Road in Neshoba County, Mississippi. Andrew Goodman, a twenty year old Queens College student; James Chaney, a Negro born and raised in Meridian, Mississippi; and Michael Schwerner, a New York City social worker. On June 20th the trio arrived in Meridian, but within twenty-four hours they had disappeared. For six tense weeks the search for the three missing civil rights workers went on; On August 4th their bodies were dug out of an earthen dam.

Mickey Schwerner's wife and parents tried hard to have Mickey's body buried in Mississippi along side that of James Chaney, only to discover that interracial burials are prohibited in Mississippi, unless perhaps beneath a dam.

When a memorial service for the three was held next to the charred ruins of the Mt. Zion Methodist Church, Sheriff Rainey and Deputy Price came to watch and listen. Young Ben Chaney gave one of the talks, saying with tears running down his cheeks, 'I want us all to stand up here together and say just one thing. I want the Sheriff to hear this good. We ain't scared no more of Sheriff·Rainey!'"

Jack Mendelsohn, <u>The Martyrs</u>

There is a street in Itta Bena called Freedom,
There is a town in Mississippi called Liberty,
There is a department in Washington called Justice.

A sign in the COFO office

"We suppose that the people who murdered Mickey and Andrew and James were not like us, not like most people in the country. I think that's a deep mistake, that we don't understand the implication of that. People keep asking me, 'Do you think that they will get convicted?' It seems that our experience will tell us that they cannot be convicted. For them to be convicted would be for society to condemn itself and that's very hard for society to do -- any society.

"The jury that votes together to decide whether or not the eighteen or twenty people who evidently got together and sat down and then planned and then got up and then murdered, that jury is like them. That's a hard thing to understand in this country."

Bob Moses speaking at the 5th Anniversary of SNCC

We Got A Thing Going On

Words and Music: SCLC

This song was made up by young people in Green County, Alabama, but it tells about the kind of "thing" going on all over the South.

"Deep in the America nobody wants to see, SNCC staffers have learned a great deal about themselves and about others. Their program is a reflection of experiences paid for by blood and pain since the sit-in movement. SNCC concentrated in the beginning on lunch counter desegregation. 'But we soon discovered', Prathia Hall says, 'that that was not where it was at.' Then we went into the Black Belt with voter registration. The people there couldn't eat at lunch counters because they were only making twenty-three cents an hour. That was where it was at.' SNCC shifted its emphasis from hamburgers to political power, using voter registration as a tool to reorganize communities and re-structure them around new axes. In out-of-the-way places, without trumpets, the original sixteen SNCC workers clawed toeholds and hung on. They went from one filthy jail to another, from one shack to another -- and as they moved, singing, their numbers grew.

Mississippi, which is criss-crossed today with a beehive of indigenous political and economic movements, is a tangible testimonial to SNCC's community organization concept."

Lerone Bennett Jr.
SNCC: Rebels With a Cause

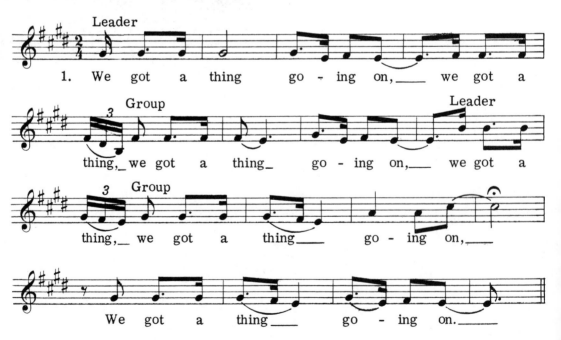

LEAD	GROUP

We got a thing going on
We got a thing   we got a thing going on,
We got a thing   we got a thing going on,
  We got a thing going on.

What kind of thing?   a voter-registration thing going on,
What kind of thing?   a voter-registration thing going on,
What kind of thing?   a voter-registration thing going on,
  We got a thing going on.

Tell the world   tell the world we got a thing going on...
etc.

What will we get   we're gonna get our freedom...
etc.

It has landed   it has landed in Georgia...
         (Alabama)
         (Mississippi)
         etc.

We got a thing   we got a thing going on...

"I question America"
> Mrs. Fannie Lou Hamer
> 1964 Democratic Convention

"The 15th Amendment of the United States Constitution commands that no person shall be deprived of the right to vote by reason of race or color. It was added to the Constitution nearly a hundred years ago. In 1867, more than 60,000 Negroes were on Mississippi's voting rolls.

"By 1892, there were only 8,500 Negroes registered. What happened between 1867 and 1892 is a nightmare in the American Dream.

"For more than a generation, in reprisal to Reconstruction, Mississippi turned life for the Negro into hell. It was a period of lynchings, armed attacks, economic harassment and other crimes -- efficiently calculated to keep the Negro away from the ballot box. The theory worked perfectly. With the opposition crushed, white Mississippians drafted a new constitution which was never submitted to the voters for ratification. The new instrument simply disenfranchised the Negro by establishing literacy qualifications which few were able to pass and poll taxes which the majority couldn't afford to pay. Since 1890, these various devices and a number of other refinements have kept more than ninety percent of Negro Mississippians in what amounts to a condition of servitude.

"In 1961, the decision was made by young freedom workers to attack the tradition that the Negro could be kept emasculated as long as he was kept politically silent. So, voter registration for Mississippi's black, second-class citizens began, first in the southwest part of the state, then in the northern Delta country. The advance has been painful and slow.

"1963 produced a mock election in Mississippi which set the tone for the 1964 Summer Project. While white Mississippians voted for a white governor, black Mississippians voted for their own man -- Aaron Henry. More than 83,000 Negroes throughout the state voted, all but a few for the first time in their lives. That proved that Negroes wanted to vote.

"The Freedom Democratic Party was established in Jackson, the state capitol, on April 26, 1964. The party was open to all races. A 'Freedom' voter-registration application was drawn up, a much-simplified version of the booby-trapped regular form. Party apparatus was organized at precinct meetings in twenty-six counties in July; thirty-five county conventions followed, and finally there was a state convention in Jackson."

> From Reports - the Challenge
> National Council of Churches
> Commission on Religion & Race

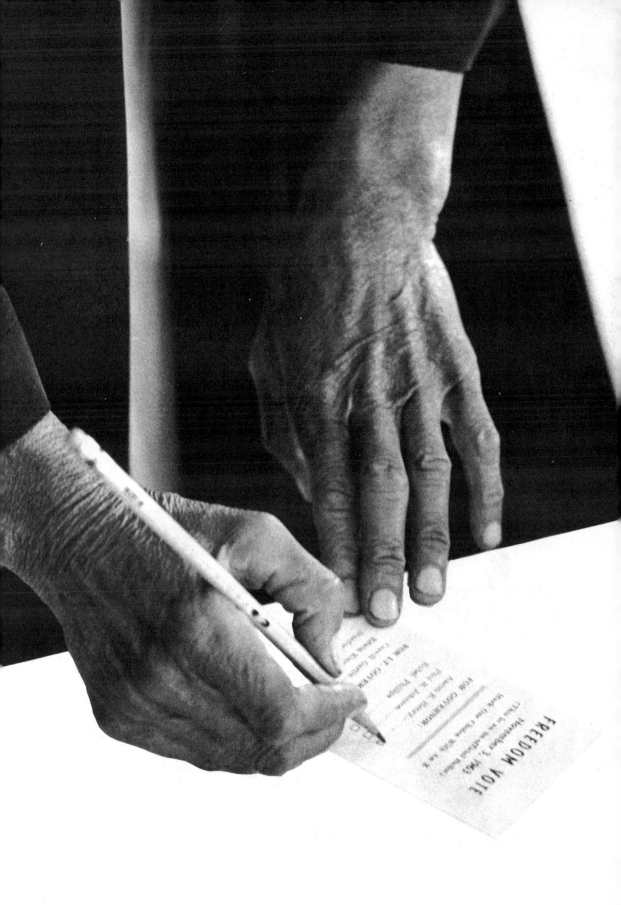

FREEDOM VOTE
November 3, 1963
(This is an un-official ballot.)
Mark (one Choice with an x

FOR GOVERNOR:
Aaron E. Henry
Paul B. Johnson
Rubel Phillips

FOR LT. GOVERNOR:
Edwin King
Carroll Gartin

Go Tell It On The Mountain

Adaptions of old spiritual
by Mrs. Hamer & Carlton Reese

"From the floor of the State Convention of the Mississippi Democratic Party:

This is the most exciting, moving and impressive thing that I have ever had the pleasure of witnessing -- let alone be a part of.

Miss Ella Baker presented a very stirring keynote address. She put great stress upon the fact that these people here today have braved extreme danger and now must redouble their efforts to get all their neighbors to join them in this struggle for Freedom.

Right after Miss Baker's speech, there was a march of all the delegates around the convention hall -- singing freedom songs, waving American flags, banners and county signs. This was probably the most soul-felt march ever to occur in a political convention, I felt, as we marched with a mixture of sadness and joy -- of humility and pride -- of fear and courage, singing 'Go Tell it on the Mountain', 'Ain't Gonna Let Nobody Turn Me 'Round', and 'This Little Light of Mine'. You would just about have to be here to really feel and see what this means to the people who are here."

Letters from Mississippi

Chorus

Go tell it on the mountain, o-ver the hills and ev'-ry-where, Go tell it on mountain To let my peo-ple go! O, Paul and Si-las bound in jail, Let my peo-ple go! O, had no mo-ney to go their bail, Let my peo-ple go.

Birmingham version

CHORUS:
Go tell it on the mountain, over the
hills and everywhere,
Go tell it on the mountain, to let my
people go.

Who's that yonder dressed in red?
Let my people go,
It must be the children Bob Moses
led,
Let my people go.

Who's that yonder dressed in
black?...
It must be the Uncle Toms turning
back...

Who's that yonder dressed in blue?
It must be the registrars coming
through...

CHORUS:
Go tell it on the mountain, over the
hills and everywhere*
Go tell it on the mountain, that
freedom is coming soon. Halleluia

You know I would not be Governor
Wallace
I'll tell you the reason why,
I'd be afraid my Lord might call me
And I would not be ready to die.
Halleluia

Oh I would not be Mayor Boutwell....

Oh I would not be Barry Goldwater....

Oh I would not be the segregationists....

*In some choruses this becomes every-every-everywhere.

In late August the Mississippi Freedom Democratic Party went to the national convention of the Democratic Party in Atlantic City, New Jersey.

"What happened between August 23 and 26, went beyond the greatest expectations of all those young people who had trudged the backroads with their registration forms, worrying about quotas. It justified all the dreams of developing indigenous leadership in black Mississippi. There, by the sea, across from a huge billboard with a picture of Barry Goldwater and the inscription 'In your heart you know he's right', a band of people from nowhere brought the machinery of a powerful national party to a halt for four days. They told their stories of oppression and terror -- Mrs. Hamer, fired the day she registered, later beaten unconscious for voter registration work -- while the Credentials Committee listened and the Mississippi regulars made feeble replies.

"The Credentials Committee finally offered a compromise (after much behind-the-scenes politicing) which provided for the seating of the regulars; the recognition of Dr. Aaron Henry and Rev. Ed King as delegates at large from the FDP and all others as honored guests; a promise that the Democratic National Committee would obligate states to select delegates for 1968 in a non-discriminatory way and that it would establish a special committee to aid states in meeting this standard.

"The Freedom Democrats rejected the compromise, in the face of arguments voiced by such national figures as Bayard Rustin and Martin Luther King. There was a sit-in on the convention floor by the FDP.

"The compromise was rejected for several reasons. The two seats were considered token recognition -- and the Negro people of Mississippi had seen too much tokenism in their time. They had come there as true representatives, not as 'delegates at large.' The compromise still recognized the regulars, despite the mass of evidence to prove they had no business there. The promises for 1968 offered no genuine relief because they referred only to Negroes already registered; even if a few Negroes could attend party meetings four years later, the people were no more likely than before to have a voice in decision making. The compromise contained no precedent for eventual recognition or patronage. To the FDP, it was a one-shot affair -- their anguish, their demands, their cause, were not."

Elizabeth Sutherland, Letters from Mississippi

"When a man has risked his life to vote, you can't offer him less than what he needs and be relevant."

Prathia Hall, SNCC

Carry It On

Words and Music - Gil Turner

Some summer volunteers decided to stay on in Mississippi.

"Dear Mom and Dad,

As I write this letter I am on the roof of our headquarters observing a sunset I cannot even begin to describe. The hills of red dirt, the pine woods, the mountains and shacks silhouetted against the blood-red sun and clouds, all this and the rest of it takes my breath away. Now and at all such times I find myself possessed by a deep melancholy, a heart-rending feeling for the black and white toilers of this state; both victims of a system that they neither created nor flourish under.

There have been incidents of violence and intimidation but they hardly seem worth noting at a time like this. I only know that I must carry on this struggle that other people have died in, and that some day that system will be changed..."

<u>*Letters from Mississippi*</u>

There's a man by my side a-walk-in', There's a voice in-side me a-talk-in', There's a word needs a-say-in', Car-ry it on ____ Car-ry it on, ____ Car-ry it on, ____ Car-ry it on. ____

There's a man by my side walkin'
There's a voice inside me talkin',
There's a word needs a-saying',
Carry it on, carry it on,
Carry it on, carry it on.

They will tell their lyin' stories
Send their dogs to bite our bodies
They will lock us in prison,
Carry it on, carry it on,
Carry it on, carry it on.

All their lies be soon forgotten,
All their dogs will lie there rottin'
All their prison walls will crumble,
Carry it on, carry it on,
Carry it on, carry it on.

If you can't go on any longer
Take the hand held by your brother
Every victory gonna bring another,
Carry it on, carry it on,
Carry it on, carry it on.

I BEEN IN
THE STORM SO LONG

The Roots

Dance and Play Songs
Work Songs
Blues
Spirituals

The people are our teachers. People who have struggled to support themselves and large families, people who have survived in Georgia and Alabama and Mississippi, have learned some things we need to know. There is a fantastic poetry in the lives of the people who have survived with strength and nobility. I am convinced of how desparately America needs the blood transfusion that comes from the Delta of Mississippi."

Prathia Hall, SNCC

"We all know that you can't trust a Negro on a negotiating committee who doesn't like his people's music. We found that out in Birmingham."

Rev. Andrew Young, SCLC

"One of the interesting developments in the South today is a new movement for the revival of true Negro folk music and other old cultural forms, such as dance and story. The moving force comes from young Southern Negroes who have come out of the freedom movement. Possessed of an inner freedom and sense of dignity won in struggle, they no longer feel ashamed of traditions of the past and have suddenly discovered a beauty and strength in the culture of their forefathers. They have determined that it not be lost.

"The emphasis is not at all on selling the rest of the country on the value of Southern Negro culture. That has already been done.

"Negroes have given the world a universal language in their music. Everywhere people want to hear ragtime, jazz, blues, gospel music, but the root forms from which this music springs are being lost. Many Negro singers from the South draw big audiences all over the country -- some of them promoted by commercial interests seeking profits, some by sincere folklorists and folk music lovers. But the people back home still think this music is something to be ashamed of.

"The most immediate aim of this new movement is to bring the music produced by the Southern Negro back to the children of those who produced it."

Anne Braden, <u>The Southern Patriot</u>
reporting on a conference on grass roots
cultural revival at Highlander, 1965

"The only place where we could say we did not like slavery, say it for ourselves to hear, was in these old songs. We could not read and the master thought he could trap us with no existence and we could do nothing about it. But we did -- even as children -- with the music. And it is our own; it came from ourselves.

These old-time songs were sung way back when our fore-parents didn't know one note from another. These songs was handed down to them, and we're still singing them the way that they did, and there's people taking note of it.

We're teaching you, telling you where we came from with these songs. Our children, and your children, are all coming on up. They call us the old-time. You know, they'll call y'all old-time someday too. I'm just going to stay old like this and let you people know where those songs you're singing now came from. You get it all so you'll know where the foundation is. You got to know the bottom before you know the top. Then you'll know where you're at.

In my time when I was coming up we had plays -- ring plays of different types. And those old ring plays sometimes meant a whole lot to the people and what they had to say and what they wanted to do. We had a play -- there used to be four of us would stand in a circle and skip across and swing one another:"

Bessie Jones of the Georgia Sea Island Singers speaking at a conference to introduce young freedom workers to root material - Atlanta, 1964.

112

Where Ya Go Lily

Bessie Jones - Ludlow

Where ya go Lily, oh sometimes,
I'm gonna rule our ruler, oh sometimes,
I'm gonna rule my master, oh sometimes,
I'm gonna rule him with a hickory, oh sometimes,
I'm gonna rule him with a shotgun, oh sometimes,
Where ya go Lily, oh sometimes....

Throw Me Anywhere, Lord

Bessie Jones - Ludlow Music

"Way back in the old times they made up this buzzard lope. They'd show how the buzzard would go around his prey -- his mule or his horse. In those days they'd throw them out in the fields and woods and things. The buzzard, when he see something dead, he'd hop around it to be sure it was dead -- look at it, step over it, dance around it, and finally pick it up.

So the people felt the same way. When they died they wasn't buried in the beautiful cemetaries like white folks, but they said in their mind that it didn't matter what they did with their bodies. If Jesus could be put in Golgotha field, I can be put in any field -- throw me anywhere -- just so my soul will be saved. "

Bessie Jones

When the SNCC Freedom Singers heard this song at a folk festival in the sea islands, they added new verses and sang, 'throw me anywhere in that old jail..."

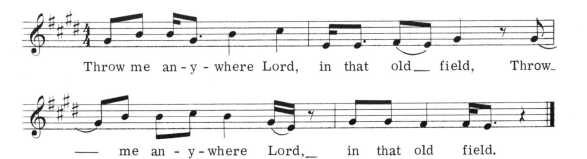

Throw me an-y-where Lord, in that old field, Throw me an-y-where Lord, in that old field.

Throw me anywhere Lord, in that
old field,
Throw me anywhere Lord, in that
old field.

You can beat and bang me, in that
old field,
You can beat and bang me, in that
old field.

Don't care how you do me...
Since my Jesus call me...

Don't care how you treat me...
Since my Jesus need me...

You can kick and stomp me...
You can kick and stomp me...

Throw me anywhere Lord...

Juba

Bessie Jones, John Davis - Ludlow Music

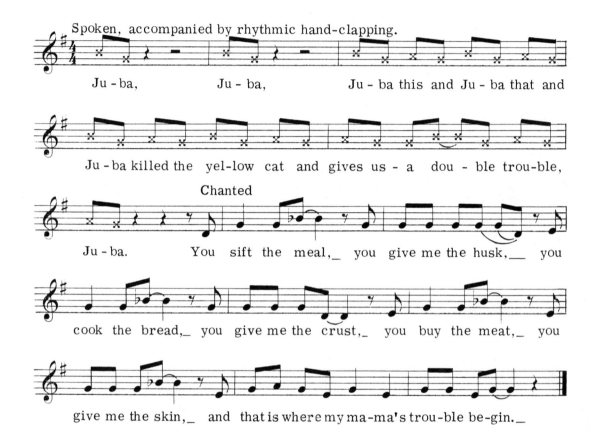

You sift the meal, you give me the husk,
You bake the bread, you give me the crust,
You cook the meat, you give me the skin,
And that's where my mama's trouble begin.

Juba, Juba, you give me double-trouble juba.
Juba-this, and juba-that, and juba killed the yellow cat. *
Juba-up and juba-down and juba all around the town,
Juba.

Massa killed the big old duck and give us all the bones to suck,
Massa killed the big old goose and give us all the bones to chew.

My old massa promised me, when he died he'd set me free.
He lived 'til his head got slick and bald
He give up the notion of dying at all.

116   *white person

"Juba -- that's giblets. The white people used to pass on the giblets to the colored folk. My grandfather told me when he was a slave they all used to eat out of one big trough. I've seen a trough like that too, so I know it's true.

Give Me The Gourd
To Drink Water

© Journal of American Folklore

Leader

- Reg - u - lar, reg - u - lar roll - ing un - der,_

Chorus   Leader

Give me the gourd to drink wa - ter, Reg-u-lar, reg-u-lar

roll-ing un - der_ Give me the gourd to drink wa - ter.

CHORUS:
Regular, regular, rolling under
Oh, give me the gourd to drink water.
Regular, regular rolling under
Give me the gourd to drink water.

Don't want no gourd for snow water*
Give me the gourd to drink water
Don't want no gourd for snow water
Give me the gourd to drink water.

Oh see what Jesus want with me,
Give me the gourd...
He take me down and set me free,
Give me the gourd....

Well I never seen the like since I
 been born....
Well the bull frog's sittin' on the
 milk cow's horn...

Oh some of these days and it won't
 be long...
Look for me but I'll be gone...

*white people's water

"Someone said that the old people used to sing songs to help themselves, to make themselves feel good anyhow and let the people know that they really knew what was going on. They had feelings.

In the old times they wouldn't let us drink out of a dipper. The white people had glass dippers, but they give us a gourd to drink water, because they figured that a gourd was just right for the colored people. They didn't know the gourd was cool -- cooler than the dipper was. They give us the best thing. We sing a song about it. "

Bessie Jones

WORK SONGS

"These songs came from an experience of some thirty years ago in my life when I was a prisoner in the Texas prison system. I had many experiences that are unique only to those who have had the opportunity -- or the curse -- of being a part of the state of Texas house of correction.

These songs came to me at the close of a period in Texas prison life when the mark of a good guard was how cruel or brutal he could be to his prisoners. Usually he was the lowest class of man that could be found -- whose only desire was to get the feel that goes with somebody calling you Boss Man.

There's a man who was known in the prison as Bullyin' Jack-a-Diamonds. He was about 70 years old when I was there. He was assistant captain on the farm and had spent some 35 to 40 years there. He was very cruel. He had a record of killing every man that escaped from his farm. One time thirteen Mexicans escaped and he followed them until he had captured them with the help of a dog. It is reported that he killed the thirteen Mexicans and he was so mad that he shot his horse and put his saddle on his own back and came back to camp."

Doc Reese, speaking to young
freedom workers at a conference
on Negro folk music at Edwards, Mississippi, 1965.

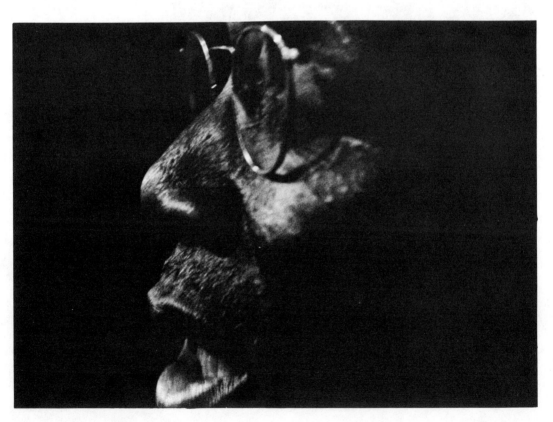

Bullyin' Jack-A-Diamonds

Traditional song as sung by Doc Reese

Bull-yin' Jack-a - Dia-monds oh my Lord

Bull-yin' Jack-a - Dia - monds oh my Lord.____

He's a num -ber one_ driv - er, Lord

He's a num-ber one driv - er oh my Lord.___

Bullyin Jack-a-Diamonds, oh my
    Lord.
Bullyin Jack-a-Diamonds, oh my
    Lord.

If you walk, he'll drive you, oh my
    Lord, (2x)

He's a number one driver, oh...

He'll drive you to your number,
    oh....

Tell me what is your number, oh....

I have a number like a thousand,
    oh....

I'm a number one roller...

But I'm rocking easy....

I'm rocking but I'm worried...

I'm worried about my baby....
She's driving me crazy...

Tell me what you call your baby...

I call my baby Mary...
I don't believe Jack-a-Diamonds is a
    natural man,
If he was seem like he would under-
    stand.

Captain, oh captain, please let me
    down,
I don't believe I can make it for
    another round.

Go Down Old Hannah

Traditional song as sung by Doc Reese

"Every day but Sunday was work day. If it was raining we'd work in the mud -- some eleven miles in a fast trot. The horses was the only thing they was concerned with because they say if you kill a nigger, we'll get another; if you kill a mule we'd have to buy another, so don't kill the mule.

They worked us from the very peak of day until black dark, and would've worked us later but there was a danger of losing somebody. Those who were convicted were always ready; if the boss turned his eye the wrong direction, they were gone.

During this time there were some twenty squads in the field, and there were usually twenty men in each squad. Each squad was guarded by a man who had a six shooter or a Winchester or a double-barrelled shotgun. Each twenty squads had two squads of dogs -- one in front and one behind -- and there were at least two dog sergeants and an assistant captain that followed us wherever we might be working.

Finally at the very close of the day, as the sun began to show herself toward the western horizon, somebody in the field would start 'Old Hannah'."

Doc Reese

Very freely

Why don't you go down old Han - nah,

well, well, well, don't you rise no more, __

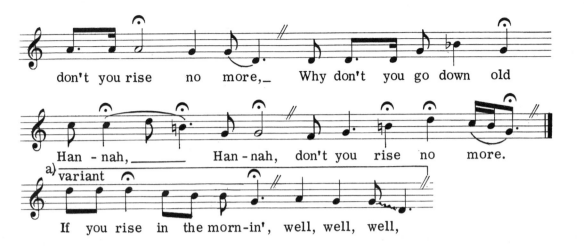

don't you rise no more,_ Why don't you go down old

Han - nah,_____ Han - nah, don't you rise no more.

a) variant

If you rise in the morn-in', well, well, well,

Why don't you go down old Hannah,
  well, well, well,
Don't you rise no more, don't you
  rise no more,
Why don't you go down old Hannah,
  Hannah,
Don't you rise no more.

If you rise in the morning,
  well, well, well,
Bring judgement sure, bring
  judgement sure,
If you rise in the morning,
  morning,
Bring judgement sure.

Well, I looked at old Hannah, well,
  well, well,
She was turning red, she was...
Then I looked at my partner, partner,
He was almost dead.

You should-a been on this old Brazos,
  well....
Back in 19 and 04,....
You could find a dead man, ...
Layin' across your row.

Why don't you wake up old dead man,
  well...
Help me carry my row,...
  (repeat)

You should-a been on this old river,
  well...
Nineteen and ten,...
You could find them workin'
the women,
and killin' the men.

My mother called me,...
And I answered M'am,...
She said ain't you tired of rolling,...
Rolling for that old sun-down man?

Then my father he called me,...
And I answered Sir,...
He said if you're tired of rolling,...
What do you stay here for.

Then my sister she called me,...
And I answered hey,...
She said ain't you tired of rolling,...
Why don't you run away.

Then my brother he called me,...
And I answered huh,
He said if you're tired of rolling,...
You know you got too long.

I got a letter from the Governor, ...
What do you think he said,...
He said he'd give me a pardon,...
If I didn't frop dead.

123

Clarksdale, Mississippi
July 5, 1964
10 A.M.

"Hot already. Like Grandmother's kitchen on a summer day when she was heating irons in a tub of coals and cooking on the wood-burning stove at the same time. It is what one would expect, however, in the Mississippi Delta and in Clarksdale, ' the blues capital of the world'.

"I've been traveling through the country that birthed Robert Johnson, Muddy Waters, Charlie Patton, Eli Green, Son House, Skip James, and Fred McDowell. It's flat, except for the trees protruding from the earth occasionally. All one sees is cotton -- from the edge of the highway to the horizon ---- cotton. Sometimes a shack can be seen from the highway, but it merely looks like a different kind of cotton plant. Nothing takes your awareness away from the Delta. It is sky, land and heat ---- each one a plane that stretches interminably and relentlessly. Even the highway is the minimum, the essence of a highway. It is narrow and, unlike the super highways, Highway 61 does not impress itself on the surroundings. Like the blues, The Delta is life in its essentialness. Sky and land. It is one line repeated twice and a rhyming last line --- succint and more than adequate in its expression."

Julius Lester,
Blues Pilgrimage: A Mississippi Diary

Delta Blues

Words and Music: Julius Lester
© by Julius Lester 1964
Assigned to Ryerson Music Pub. 1966

I'd rather drink muddy water,
Sleep out a hollow log
I'd rather drink muddy water,
Sleep out a hollow log,
Than to be in Mississippi
Livin' like a dirty dog.

It's down in the Delta,
Cotton up to my front door (2x)
Time the bugs and the white men
  get there
It ain't surprisin' I'm poor.

Thirty cents an hour
And I'm over twenty-one (2x)
And you know my mother told me
That my life had just begun.

Mary had a baby
But I don't believe it's mine (2x)
Baby's got blue eyes
And his hair's just a little too fine.

Tougaloo, Mississippi
July 13, 1964
early a.m.

"It's raining now and night has emerged from the all day greyness. Helen and I are drinking bourbon as I show her how to finger an e minor chord. It doesn't matter that she won't learn to play it tonight. It doesn't matter that she has a difficult time carrying a tune when I don't sing with her. I don't know if I can say what does matter. Maybe the bourbon. It can do something that we can't. It can obliterate the thought of half of a man's body draped over a log in the river. It can make me not care about the 4000 and more lynchings that have occurred in my native land. It can make me forget how long and empty a Mississippi highway is at night; how few houses there are and how many miles and miles of forests there are with dirt roads disappearing into them. How much hate can one individual feel directed at him before his soul fills with a sadness that penetrates even his happy moments?

"She is an old woman and I am an old man and the same trees from which so many Negroes have hung are being washed by the rain tonight. The rain beats on the roofs of the lynched and the lynchers. It soaks into the charred wood of a bombed church and runs down the stained glass windows of another. The grass is green on the banks of the rivers, but when you go fishing take along a winding sheet.

"It is late now and I must sleep. There isn't much any one man can do in this life, but each man should do what he has to and when he has to. Sometimes it is nothing more than making a pilgrimage. Another time it will be nothing more than dying.

'I got to keep moving, I got to keep moving,
    blues falling down like hail,
    blues falling down like hail,
Uuhh, blues falling down like hail,
    blues falling down like hail,
And the day keeps on 'minding me there's a
    hellbound on my trail,
    hellbound on my trail,
    hellbound on my trail. '

(Robert Johnson)

"If it must be, so be it. "

Julius Lester,
Blues Pilgrimage: A Mississippi Diary

Bourgeois Blues

Words and Muisc: Huddie Ledbetter
Publisher: Folkways Music Publishers

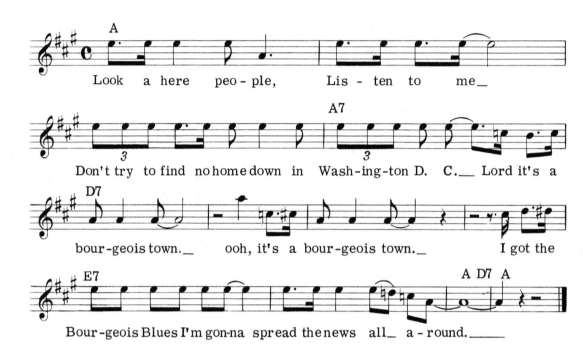

Look a here peo-ple, Lis-ten to me_
Don't try to find no home down in Wash-ing-ton D. C._ Lord it's a
bour-geois town._ ooh, it's a bour-geois town._ I got the
Bour-geois Blues I'm gon-na spread the news all_ a-round.____

Look-a here people, Listen to me
Don't try to find no home down in
Washington D. C.

CHORUS:
Lord it's a bourgeois town. . . . . oooh,
It's a bourgeois town.
I got the Bourgeois Blues
I'm gonna spread the news all around.

Me and Martha was standin' upstairs,
I heard a white man say, 'Don't want
no colored up there. '

CHORUS

Home of the brave, land of the free,
I don't want to be mistreated by no
bourgeoisie.

CHORUS

White folks in Washington, they know
how,
Throw a colored man a nickel to see
him bow.

CHORUS

Tell all the colored folks to listen to
me,
Don't try to find a home in
Washington D. C.

CHORUS

Leadbelly, "King of the 12-string guitar," and his songs are recognized not only across the country, but around the world. In Shreveport, Louisiana, however, he is virtually unknown or considered just somebody's old uncle who picked a guitar. Gradually more and more young people in the South, including freedom workers, are hearing about him and beginning to know some of his songs like "Take This Hammer", "Midnight Special", "Goodnight Irene" and "Cotton Fields Back Home".

"...They that walked in darkness sang songs of the olden days -- Sorrow Songs -- for they were weary at heart. There are people who tell us that life was joyous then for the black slave, careless and happy. But not all the past South, though it rose from the dead, can gainsay the heart-touching witness of these songs. They are the music of an unhappy people, of the children of disappointment; they tell of death and suffering and unvoiced longing toward a truer world. In these songs the slave spoke to the world. Such a message is naturally veiled and half articulate.

"Through all the sorrow of the Sorrow Songs there breathes a hope --a faith in the ultimate justice of things. The minor cadences of despair change often to triumph and calm confidence. Sometimes it is faith in life, sometimes a faith in death, sometimes assurance of boundless justice in some fair world beyond. But which-ever it is, the meaning is always clear: that sometime, somewhere, men will judge men by their souls and not their skins..."

> W.E.B. DuBois, of "The Sorrow Songs"
> The Souls of Black Folk, 1903

"SNCC workers identify themselves totally with the people --
the poor, the despised, the downtrodden, the humiliated.
Sharecroppers with eyes, victims with voices, they thrust
themselves into the ditches of desperation so they can speak
more clearly for the inhabitants thereof."

Lerone Bennett Jr.
SNCC: Rebels With A Cause

"Basically, we're dealing with poor people, and they are the
people we identify with. It even affects our salary scale. One
reason it's so low is just lack of money, but another reason is
that we think you can't come out from a nice hotel every day to
work with these people and then go back at night. Besides, in
Mississippi, as a practical matter, you have to look like a
rural Negro in order to get to talk to a rural Negro. And then
we have to move a lot, and there's no use wearing a coat and
tie if you're likely to end up sleeping on the floor. Another
thing that's operating here too, consciously or unconsciously,
is: Why should we have to comb our hair and put on a coat and
tie to get what are basically our rights? The student sit-in
movement was positive, and without it we couldn't have had
this, but it was also defensive -- to show people we were
clean. This is a different game. Also, there's a certain
mystique about the dress (overalls, rough shoes, etc.), a
certain morale factor. Maybe we've overdone it; it's almost
a uniform now."

James Forman, SNCC

Down On Me

Moving Star Hall - Johns Island, S.C.

CHORUS:
Down on me, Lord, down on me,
Seems like everybody in this whole
wide world is
Down on me.

When I get to heaven, gonna sing and
shout,
Nobody there gonna put me out.
Seems like everybody in this whole
wide world is
Down on me.

I've been 'buked and I've been scorned
I've been talked about sure's you're
born.
Seems like....

You can talk about me just as much
as you please
The more you talk, I'm gonna bend
my knees.
Seems like....

I Been In The Storm So Long

Moving Star Hall, Johns Island, South Carolina

I've _____ been in ____ the storm _____ so

long ___ You know I've been in ____ the storm _____ so

long ___ Sing-in' Oh, Lord ___ give me more time _ to pray ___ I've

been in ____ the storm _____ so ___ long. _____

*

I am __ a moth - er - less child, ___ Sing - in'

I am __ a moth - er - less child, ____ Sing - in'

Oh, Lord, ____ give me more time __ to pray, ____ I've

been in ____ the storm ___ so ___ long. _____

* *This melody most often used for additional verses.*

134

I been in the storm so long,
You know, I been in the storm so long,
Singin' oh Lord, give me more time to
   pray,
You know I been in the storm so long.

This is a needy time...

Look what a shape I'm in...

Mend all my wicked ways...

I am a motherless child...

Lord, I need you now...

I been in the storm so long...

"Some of us, because we can read a little bit more, forget about the place we came from and some of the songs which motivate us to go on. I remember an old woman who worked on a plantation all her life. Some days she would look up at the sun and sing 'nobody knows the trouble I've seen' or 'I been in the storm so long'. When older folks have sung those songs, it helped them realize they're trusting in God and reaching for a better day.

Regardless of how well a person can sing the classical songs and opera, they don't have that feeling of people who sang from oppressed soul and need. Those songs come from the soul. Even if it was the blues, it's sweet because it comes from a person that is in need for something and is longing for decency and friendship.

Now if we hide those sweet songs and try to get away from what we came from, what will we tell our children about the achievement we have made and the distance we have come?"

Esau Jenkins, Johns Island, S. C.

Go Down Moses

John Davis of the Georgia Sea Island Singers

(God told him)   (Go)
   Go down brother Moses,   Way down in Egypt land,
Tell old brother Pharoah, to let my children go.

I'm gonna take you by your hand, let my children go,
I'm gonna take you home to the promised land, let my children go.

When the children leave Egypt, they dressed in red, let my children go,
Well you know it was the children which Moses led, let my children go.

Moses

John Davis, Ludlow Music

Oh Mo-ses, Mo-ses, don't you let King Pha-roah o-ver-take you,_ Mo-ses, Mo-ses, don't you let King Pha-roah o-ver-take you, Mo-ses, Mo-ses, don't you let King Pha-roah o-ver-take you, In some lone-some grave - yard._____

Moses, Moses, Don't you let king Pharoah overtake you
Moses, Moses, Don't you let king Pharoah overtake you
Moses, Moses, Don't you let king Pharoah overtake you,
In some lonesome graveyard.

Moses, Moses, I heard the horses running....

Moses, Moses, I heard the children grumbling....

Moses, Moses, I heard old Jordan rolling...

Jordan, Jordan, let my children cross over...

Moses, Moses, I heard the angels moaning...

Mother, Mother, don't you let your daughter condemn you...

Moses, Moses, I hear the thunder rolling...

I'll Be All Right

Traditional - Adapted by food & tobacco workers,
Charleston, S.C. 1945

*The anthym of the Civil Rights Movement. "We Shall Overcome, "
was originally "I'll Be All Right" and came out of the Negro
Church. It began to evolve as a 'freedom song' as early as
1945, during a strike of the Food and Tobacco Workers in
Charleston, South Carolina.*

*"It was a nasty strike, through five and a half months of a
rough, rainy and cold winter. It began with 500 to 600 people,
mostly Negroes, picketing every day from 7:30 in the morning
'til 6:30 at night. Eventually people got tired and morale became low. Many people went back to work as the winter
turned so cold and rainy.*

*"To keep up morale, the remaining pickets would 'sing them-
selves away' some days. We sang I'll be all right, ... we will
win our rights ... we will win this fight ... the Lord will see
us through ... we will overcome. We sang it with a clap and
a shout until sometimes the cops would quiet us down.*

*"Eventually the strike was won on a national level. We were
relieved to see the spring of 1946 finally come, and we went
back to work. "*

Lillie May Marsh, one of the picket captains

*Two of the picketers from Charleston took the song to High-
lander where it became the theme song. Zilphia Horton carried
it all over the south and introduced it to many labor unions.
Pete Seeger later took it north and sang it on college campuses.
In 1960 Guy introduced it to the sit-in movement at the first
SNCC conference in Raliegh, N.C.*

last. Well, I'll be all right___ some___ day.

I'll be all right, I'll be all right,
I'll be all right someday.
If in my heart, I do not yield,
I'll be all right someday.

I'll sing my song...

I'll overcome...

I'll Fly away...

I'm going home...

A slightly different version comes from a lady from Wagoner, S. C.

I'll be all right, I'll be all right, I'll be all
right some day._____ If in my heart, I do not
yield, I will be all right some day.

Variant a)

I'll be all right, I'll be all right

I'll be all right, I'll be all right, I'll
   be all right someday.
All of my troubles will be over, and
   I'll be free at last,
Well, I'll be all right someday.

I'm working to be all right...

I'm singing to be all right...

I'm struggling to be all right...

"Through song and dance a people are able to share their burden, triumph, sadness and gladness of heart. People sing songs of heroism. They sing songs about the common oppressor or exploiter. The smallest and the greatest desires of a people are brought out in folk music. These songs can be used to draw people together and unite them in one common aim, goal and purpose."

Willie Peacock, who organized the first
Mississippi Folk Festival, 1965

OH, WALLACE, YOU NEVER CAN JAIL US ALL

Selma, Alabama

"We want to live in peace with all mankind, and especially with the whites of the South. Our interests are identical. But we do not want the peace of the lamb with the lion...Give us our rights! Will you do this or force us away from you?"

a Negro minister in Selma, 1887

"Any form of social or educational integration is not possible within the context of our society."

Circuit Judge James A. Hare
Dallas County, 1963

"Selma does not intend to change its customs or way of life."
Chris Heinz, mayor of Selma, 1963

"You're an agitator: that's the lowest form of life."

Sheriff Jim Clark

SELMA, ALABAMA

Selma is the seat of Dallas County, Alabama. In 1961, 57 percent of the population was Negro, but only about 1 percent of the eligible Negroes were registered to vote, while 64 percent of the eligible whites were registered. In the two adjoining Black Belt counties, Wilcox and Lowndes, none of the 11,207 voting age Negroes were registered.

Bernard Lafayette and his wife Colia came to Selma to begin a voter registration drive for SNCC.

"Colia and I first went to Selma in February, 1963. It was sort of our honeymoon; we'd been married about six weeks. The first SNCC worker there came back and said that we might as well scratch Selma off the list because the people there just weren't ready for a movement. We didn't get any different impression when we went there. We had trouble finding a place to live; most people were afraid to put us up. But we work on this assumption: no matter how bad a place is, some people got courage. Those people are gonna be warm and friendly to you.

"It was Mrs. Amelia Bounton who befriended us. We used her office and began to work. The first thing we did was to just try to get people to loosen up, to talk about registration and to realize they needed to vote. We set up classes teaching people how to fill out the registration forms. We knew that the forms are irrelevant in terms of voting and have nothing to do with whether a person is qualified to vote or not. But it's a psychological thing to build people's confidence. They have to feel themselves that they can fill out the form before they feel they can go down to try to register.

"We tried to get people around the city to come, but it was slow. So we went out in the rural. The people out there are close to the earth, they're very religious and warm and friendly. And mostly they're unafraid. They own most of their own property and their little stores. They work hard and they want to see a future for their children. So we got these people to go and try to register to vote first.

"Then we used this as a leverage to try to embarrass many of the people in the city. City folks are sometimes critical and skeptical about country people. So we pointed out that these people were really getting ahead. When these city people began to go down it was really sort of a birth of a movement.

"Between February and September we got about 2,000 people to go down and try to register and about 600 of them actually did get registered.

"By this time we had the people teaching each other. When one person learned to fill out the form, he was qualified to help somebody else. We had recruited some local workers too. We didn't really have to be there anymore.

"We went back to school that Fall. Worth Long and James Love were the SNCC workers who took over in Selma. The situation continued to develop and I would get little bits of news from there.

"In the Fall of 1964 James Bevel and SCLC moved into Alabama and began to build on making Selma a national issue of Voter Registration.

"I went back in 1965 to help with some of the planning and strategy. I saw some great changes. Many, many people had gone to jail -- people you never would have expected to stand up. Some of the kids I had worked with -- whose parents, grand-parents and teachers had all argued with them, threatened them and disciplined them -- would run up to me:

"'Guess what happened! Man, my grandmother went to jail! Man, I can't believe it...my grandma's in jail!'

"The principal of one high school who had told the kids he would lower their grades if they participated in the Movement, actually led a march of teachers asking for the right to vote. Many of the informers -- Negroes who used to carry messages downtown to the white people -- were still message-carriers, but they were now bringing messages to us. So I saw a whole city change. Large numbers of adults were participating, both from Selma and from surrounding areas.

"Then when Jimmy Lee Jackson from Marion was killed, I believe that really prompted the march. We realized that the killing would go on, based on people just demonstrating for their right to vote. Somehow we had to make the price of human life go up. People were being shot and killed and the killers were getting off pretty cheap. We felt we had to create what we call 'mass dis-location'. That's a non-violent technique where you make it uncomfortable for people by expressing your grievances in a non-violent fashion. A massive march on Montgomery had been planned for a long time, but no one had set a time-table for it. This seemed like a good time."

Bernard Lafayette, SNCC

147

Black Sunday at the River of Tears

"Moving on a serpentine path from the low hills of the north, the Alabama River runs crooked beneath the Edmund Pettus bridge, sides along Selma's Broad Street, and drifts languidly on to Montgomery. A large river, it crawls through the dry eucalyptus-dying plants at the water's edge -- worming its slow way through the red Alabama earth.

"There is little beautiful in this river. 'Alabama' is its white name, but to the Negroes of Selma and the Black Belt it is a 'river of tears'. Too many black bodies have stained its muddy waters, too many fathers, brothers, distant uncles -- now misty relations.

"And from the bridge, to the south, the land, surrendering its undulation, begins the long rich submission to the Gulf.

"It is here on this dry dusty 1920's bridge that the marchers came on Sunday. Now it is 'Black Sunday'. They came marching across, black and four abreast like pilgrims to a shrine, pulled together by their fear, massive in their purpose like some ancient Roman column. It is here just past the bridge that they were stopped, black line on the darker asphalt, headed for a vision in Montgomery.

"They knew. They must have known, for to be black and long in Alabama leaves few secrets. They knew as they paused forty seconds and as the rasp 'Troopers Advance' rang out across the dry tension, and they knew at the dull first thud upon the skull of John Lewis.

"The women fell first, for women rarely believe they will be beaten no matter how many times they are. And with the thud of billy clubs, they fell, legs askew, black thighs and legs shining in the sweat of tears. They lay upon the hot pavement and awaited the jolts from fourteen ounces of oak. They fell and even the car-hipped possemen and bellied troopers could catch an old woman. They and the children began to run in circles, and the troopers, predicting their circuits, would stand in wait and club them as they passed.

"The men, lithe, athletic on their feet, escaping at first, saw this and returned to lie across the bodies of the women and the screeching children. With the stage set, the troopers flailed at the living hulks beneath them. And when the bodies relaxed and rolled stunned, the clubs found others, and the strange tableaux, body by body, couple by couple, found its way back across the bridge toward the city.

"It was a quiet mid-spring day. Sheriff James Clark lifted his head toward the wind, methodically set his foot and fired. The bright cannister lofted gently over the heads of the streaming troopers and landed amidst the retreating demonstrators. With a hollow sound more cannisters clanked metallically on the soft asphalt, sprouting the frightening clouds of gas.

"And now, the wounded behind, the body, shucked of those who had scampered down the steep slopes of the river bank, jumped the highway barriers, avoided the hostile whites jeering, and fled across the fields to safety, this group, this body down to its core of those who were unable to run, too dazed, too unconscious to run, would not run, this body was inched back to Selma. Back from the light of the distant goal in Montgomery, back into the world a hundred years ago, back into slavery and injustice, back into Selma, this black crowd was inched, pushed, shoved, beaten, horse-prodded, back across the bridge, down Broad Street, into Sylvan, back to the church where it had begun."

Henry Hampton, To Bear Witness
Unitarian - Universalist Association

150

On Monday, March 8, 1965 (the day after Black Sunday) Martin Luther King sent telegrams to many religious groups in North America:

"In the vicious maltreatment of defenseless citizens of Selma, where old women and young children were gassed and clubbed...we have witnessed an eruption of the disease of racism which seeks to destroy all...It is fitting that all Americans help to bear the burden. I call therefore...join me in Selma...In this way all America will testify that the struggle in Selma is for the survival of democracy everywhere in our land."

The nation responded.

For many the decision to go to Selma was a difficult one to make. Rev. James Reeb was one of these for he had heavy responsibilities at home in Boston. But by early Tuesday morning he had joined the hundreds of clergymen and others who had responded to King's appeal.

After Tuesday's march Reeb and two more Unitarian ministers ate together in Walker's Cafe, a gathering place for the marchers in the Negro part of town. They left after dark and the street was already deserted. Four white men appeared from across the street and shouted "Hey niggers, hey you niggers!" just before they set upon the three ministers. Reeb was hit with a club over his left ear. "It was a two-handed swing in the style of a left handed batter, and the man's face was intense and vicious,' remembered one of the other ministers.

Forty-eight hours later James Reeb was dead.

This May Be The Last Time

Traditional spiritual
New words from Citizenship schools

James Reeb was not the first casualty in Selma. On February 26, Jimmy Lee Jackson was shot point blank in the stomach by an Alabama State Trooper. "A quiet boy whose life had been unmarked and unnoticed except by a few, was marked by history at his death. Alabama Negroes began a protest march down highway 80 from Selma to Montgomery. "

Jack Mendelsohn, The Martyrs

This may be the last time,
This may be the last time, children
This may be the last time,
It may be the last time, I don't
  know.

It may be the last time we can sing
  together,
May be the last time, I don't know
It may be the last time, we pray
  together,
May be the last time, I don't know.

It may be the last time that we walk
  together....
It may be the last time that we dance
  together...

Berlin Wall

Tune: Joshua Fit the Battle
Words: Selma Young People

A barricade, tabbed the Berlin Wall, was set up in front of Brown Chapel by the police, to define the line of restriction. The marchers were determined to get it down.

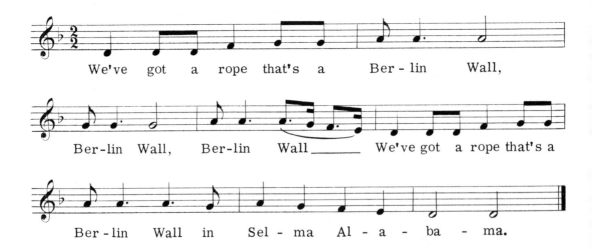

We've got a rope that's a Ber-lin Wall,
Ber-lin Wall, Ber-lin Wall____ We've got a rope that's a
Ber-lin Wall in Sel-ma Al-a-ba-ma.

We've got a rope that's a Berlin Wall,
   Berlin Wall, Berlin Wall,
We've got a rope that's a Berlin Wall,
In Selma, Alabama.

We're gonna break this Berlin Wall...

We're gonna stay here 'til it fall...

Hate is the thing that built that wall...

Old George Wallace helped build that
   wall...

Love is the thing that'll make it fall...

We're gonna stand up 'til it fall...

We've got a rope that's a Berlin Wall...

154

Somewhere between 40 and 50 thousand people gathered in Selma to express their indignation of the murders and the injustice of Alabama. For five days they marched in rain and mud, in sunshine and blisters -- fifty miles to Montgomery.

"It's ironic how I got to Selma. I was over at some Jewish friends' house and we were watching this film on television -- Judgement at Nuremburg. It's a powerful film and it ends with this question -- has everybody been captured, or will there be another war? Right after that, they bring on this newsreel showing the people in Selma getting beaten down by the possemen, and people on horses beating the people down. That was just like a crushing blow. So I felt I had to go to Selma and do something, I didn't know what."

Jimmie Collier, SCLC

Do What The Spirit Say Do

Spiritual – new words by young people in Selma

You gotta do what the spirit say do,
You gotta do what the spirit say do,
And what the spirit say do, I'm gonna
  do, Oh Lord
You gotta do what the spirit say do.

You gotta march when the spirit say
  march (2x)
And when the spirit say march, you
  better march, Oh Lord
You gotta march when the spirit say
  march.

You gotta sing...

You gotta moan...

You gotta picket...

You gotta vote...

You gotta move...

You gotta pray
        preach
        shout
        rock
        cool it
        love
        die.

"We were marching along and some old Army guys were calling cadence -- Hup, hip, to your left ... to your left, right, left. I started thinking that left isn't a thing that we want to get. I mean we want to keep up ... we want to go along ... we want to go to Montgomery which is not getting left. Right is an affirmative statement, so I said why don't we accent on the right foot. And so a-right, right, and then you can put together verses and the answers from the group would be right ... right ... right. And so I started singing:"

Len Chandler

158

Right! Right!

Words and Music - Len Chandler

Pick 'em up and lay 'em down (Right! Right!) Pick 'em up and lay 'em down, (Right! Right!) Pick 'em up and lay 'em down,___ (Right! Right!) All the way from Sel-ma town. (Right! Right!)

Pick 'em up and lay 'em down
  Right! Right!
Pick 'em up and lay 'em down
  Right! Right!
Pick 'em up and lay 'em down
  Right! Right!
All the way from Selma town.
  Right! Right!

Oh the mud was deep, Right! Right!
The hills were steep, Right, etc.
Now we've made some level ground
Let Wallace hear the sound

I've been walking so long
I've put blisters on the street
Well I caught the Freedom fever
And it settled in my feet

Did the rain come down
Well I thought I would drown
Then I thought of Sheriff Jim
Something said you'd better swim

"There was a guy named Jim Letherer who had one leg. He went all the way. There was a picture of us in the N. Y. Times and it said something about the last leg of the march. Jim said 'hey Len, make me a verse':"

Jim Letherer's leg got left
But he's still in the fight
Been walking day and night
Jim's left leg is all right

I been walking so long
I got blisters on my feet
Make me want to skip a beat
I been walking so long
My feet done turn to wheels
I don't think no more of riding
I disremember how it feels
Is freedom all.............
Right! Right!

Which Side Are You On?

Original verses by Florence Reese
© 1947 by Stormking
New verses by Len Chandler

Observers lined route 80 -- local Negroes who for one reason or another, usually fear of very real reprisals (State troopers and local police were constantly photographing local participants), did not join the march, watched silently or jubilantly, their faces conveying what this march meant to them. Whites also watched, silently or noisily with signs reading "Rent a priest, $5 per day", "Fake Clergy and Beatniks Go Home", etc.

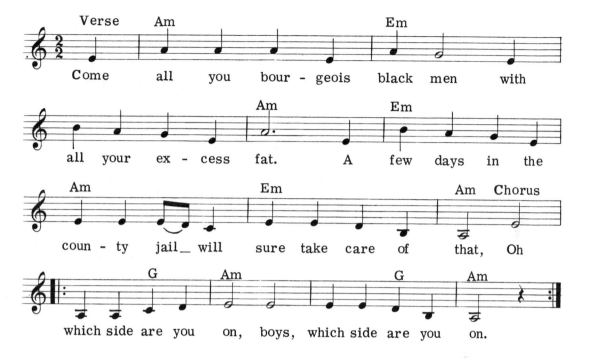

Verse

Come all you bourgeois black men with all your excess fat. A few days in the county jail will sure take care of that, Oh

Chorus

which side are you on, boys, which side are you on.

Come all you bourgeois black men
With all your excess fat
A few days in the county jail
Will sure take care of that.

Come all you northern liberals
Take a Klansman out to lunch
But when you dine, instead of wine
You should serve non-violent punch.

Come all you rough, tough bullies
Forget your knives and gun
Non-violence is the only way
The battle can be won.

Come all you high-toned college
   grads
Pronounce your final 'g's
But don't forget your grandma,
She's still scrubbin' on her knees.

Come all you Uncle Toms
Take that hankie from your head
Forget your fears and shed a tear
For the life of shame you've led.

You need not join our picket line
If you can't stand the blows
But join your dimes with dollars
Or be counted with our foes.

I heard that Gov. Wallace
Just up and lost his mind
And he bought a case of Man Tan
And joined the picket line.

They say the Ku Klux Klan
Just up and died their sheets
And now they sing "Oh Freedom"
Everytime they meet.

I've been walkin' so long
I've put blisters on the street
I've caught the freedom fever
And it's settled in my feet.

*For original verses used earlier on the Freedom Rides, etc, see
We Shall Overcome, Oak Publications.

Another Day's Journey

Traditional song – new words SCLC

"I was glad I had on dark glasses because for ten miles, tears were streaming down my cheeks. I just wasn't prepared for the overwhelming feeling of love. I didn't realize that people of every color, every background could really feel together. I was surrounded by Negro teen-agers from Montgomery, wonderful kids with a kind of pride and freedom I'd never seen before. They kept calling to the whites on the sidewalk, 'Come on and join us. We want you too!' And they really meant it."

Price Cobbs, a Negro psychiatrist
from the west coast

Well, it's an-oth-er day's_ jour-ney and I'm glad,_ I'm glad a-bout it, Well, I'm glad, I'm glad a-bout it Oh Lord, I'm glad, I'm glad a-bout it, It's an-oth-er day's_ jour-ney and I'm so glad, I'm glad a-bout it, Oh well_ I'm so glad_ to be here.

LEAD	GROUP
Well it's another day's journey and I'm glad	I'm glad about it
Well I'm glad	I'm glad about it
Oh Lord, I'm glad	I'm glad about it
Well it's another day's journey and I'm so glad	I'm glad about it
Well I'm so glad to be here.	

Well we're going to Montgomery and I'm glad   I'm glad about it
etc.   "

Gonna see Gov. Wallace...   "

I'm gonna tell him I want to be free...   "

Yes, I want the right to vote...   "

It's raining on this road, but I'm glad...   "

Ain't no rain gonna stop me...   "

Ain't no white folks gonna stop me...   "

Ain't no troopers gonna stop me...   "

Well it's another day's journey...   "

Way Over Yonder
In Montgomery

Adapted from religious song,
'Church Bells Tolling", by James Orange

"In the Negro section the streets were lined with people, many especially the old were crying silently. Everyone wanted to join, but many didn't dare. Sometimes someone would call out and explain why. 'God bless you, God bless you,' came over and over again. We were singing and victory-shouting as hard as we could, so loud that sometimes I lost breath. Sometimes we joined hands.

I was excited; I felt I was floating. It seemed to me delightfully ridiculous that the march marshall from Alabama State College should run along beside us holding up a card which read 'SMILE'. Of course I was smiling. Some of the Negroes were not. All of those from Montgomery had defied fear: fear of losing jobs, losing business, fear of losing life in a sense.

The sky was clear gray. I looked back many times but I could never see the end of the march -- or its beginning for that matter, until we reached the State House at the end of Dexter Avenue. We sat down on the street and waited for the end of the line of marchers to catch up. I read later that it took over an hour and a half. It did not occur to me that it was anything extraordinary to sing 'black and white together' in front of the Alabama State House. For that time the street belonged to us.

I was tired. 'Please call me when Martin Luther King speaks', I said and I fell asleep on the street. When I woke up a woman had covered me with a plastic dry-cleaner's bag because it had been drizzling. Dr. King was beginning to speak.

When I came home from the March, I scraped some of the thick, clayey mud from my shoes and saved it. It was as if I wanted to keep something tangible to testify for me that the extraordinary march had happened and that I was really there. This is the first inkling I have ever had of what is perhaps behind the preservation of relics."

Mrs. Theresa Fulton
art historian from California

164

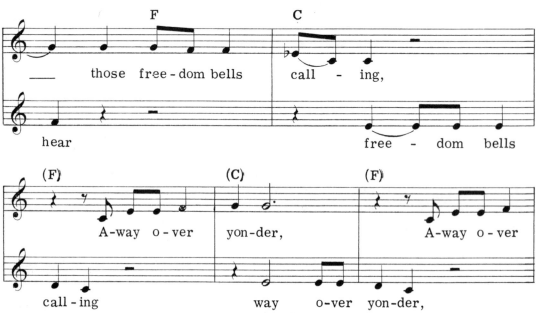

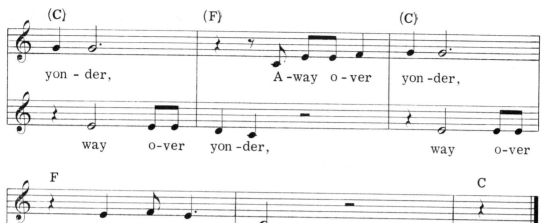

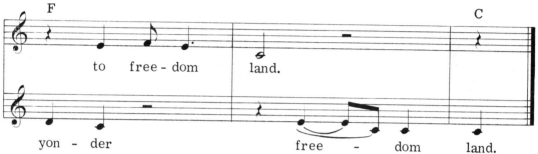

LEAD

I wonder can you hear
That freedom bell tolling
I wonder can you hear
That freedom bell tolling
I wonder can you hear
That freedom bell tolling
Way over yonder
Way over yonder
Way over yonder
In Montgomery

I wonder will you tell
Will you tell everybody (3x)
I want my freedom (3x)
Right away

There'll be no segregation
No discrimination
I'm gonna see Gov. Wallace
Won't worry about Lingo
Won't beat my head

GROUP

can you hear, can you hear
freedom bell tolling
can you hear, can you hear
freedom bell tolling
can you hear, can you hear
freedom bell tolling
way over yonder
way over yonder
way over yonder
in Montgomery

will you tell, will you tell,
tell everybody
I want my freedom
right away

way over yonder
way over yonder
way over yonder
way over yonder
way over yonder

Oh, Wallace

Tune: Kidnapper, New words: James Orange
and other young people

*"I started singing this song during the summer of 1964. When
we walked up to the capitol almost a year later -- about 40,000
people -- it felt good because this made the dream come true."*

James Orange, SCLC

Chorus (Am) (Em)
Oh __ Wal - lace, __ you nev - er can jail us all __

(Am)
Oh Wal - lace, _

(Em)
se - gre - ga - tion's bound to fall, __ da dat __ da da da

(B7) (Em)
dat da da da da da dat da dat __ da da da

Verse
dat, I said I read in the pa - per da dat __ da da da

(B7) (Em)
dat, Just the oth - er day, da dat __ da da da

dat, The Free - dom Fight - ers, da dat __ da da da

dat, They were on their way, da dat— da da da dat.

CHORUS
Oh Wallace, you never can jail us
   all....all....all,
Oh Wallace, segregation's bound to
   fall - da da dada dada da-da-da-da-
   da-da dada dada dada

I read in the paper da da dada dada
Just the other day " " " "
That freedom fighters   etc...
Are on their way
They're coming by bus
And airplane too
They'll even walk
If you ask them to.

Don't you worry about
Going to jail
'Cause Martin Luther King
Will go your bail
He'll get you out
Right on time
Put you back
On the picket-line.

I don't want no mess
I don't want no jive
And I want my freedom
In sixty-five
Listen Jim Clark
You can hear this plea
You can lock us in the house
You can throw away the key.

Now I'm no preacher
But I can tell
You've got to straighten up
Or you're bound for hell
You can tell Wilson Baker
And Al Lingo
That the people in Selma
Won't take no mo'.

Well this is the message
I want you to hear
You know I want my freedom
And I want it this year
So you can tell Jim Clark
And all those state guys too
I'm gonna have my freedom
And there's nothing they can do.

You can push me around
You can throw me away
But I still want freedom
And I want it every day
You can tell Jim Clark
And Al Lingo
It's time for them
To end Jim Crow.

Route Eighty
Is the way we'll come
I know them boys will have
A lot of fun
You might see black
And a few whites too
They're looking for freedom
Like me and you.

I saw James Orange
Just the other day
He was getting ready
To be on his way
He had a white shirt on
And some blue jeans
Just come on to Eighty
You'll see what we mean.

You know Jack and Jill went up the
   hill
And Jill came down with the Civil
   Rights Bill
Don't want no shuckin', don't want
   no jive
Gonna get my freedom in sixty-five.

SUNDAY NIGHT

"It was with great optimism that we marched from Selma to Montgomery. The more than forty thousand pilgrims had marched across a route travelled by Sherman a hundred years before. But in contrast to a trail of destruction and bloodshed, they watered the red Alabama clay with tears of joy and love overflowing, even for those who taunted and jeered along the sidelines. This was certainly a triumphant entry into the 'Cradle of the Confederacy'. And an entry destined to put an end to that racist oligarchy once and for all.

"We had come to petition Governor Wallace. We had come to represent the Negro citizens of Alabama and freedom loving people from all over the United States and the world. We had come not only five days and fifty miles, but we had come from three centuries of suffering and hardship. We had come to declare that we must have our Freedom Now. We must have the Right to Vote; we must have equal protection of the law and an end to police brutality.

"What simple requests. How shameful that American citizens should have to petition a state for such elementary freedoms in the second half of the Twentieth Century. And yet, this was the climax of a three-month campaign, waged at tremendous cost in human suffering including two deaths.

"At the news of still a third murder we were reminded that this was not a march to the capitol of a civilized nation as was the March on Washington. We had marched through a swamp of poverty, ignorance, race hatred and sadism. We were reminded that the only reason that this march was possible was due to the presence of thousands of federalized troops, marshals and a Federal Court order. We were reminded that the troops would soon be going home, and that in the days to come we must renew our attempts to organize the very county in which Mrs. Liuzzo was murdered. If they will murder a white woman for standing up for the Negroes' right to vote, what will they do to Negroes who attempt to register and vote?

"We are reminded that Goveror Wallace was elected by the Klan contingent in the state, and that his administration alone had allowed ten deaths surrounding civil rights activities and twenty-three bombings, with not a single person being convicted.

"And so amidst the joys and triumphs of one of the greatest occasions produced in the ten years of nonviolent struggle, we were called down from the mountain top of hope and exaltation and into the valley of reality, 'a valley of shadow of death'."

Dr. Martin Luther King, Jr.
An Open Letter to the American People

Murder On The Road
In Alabama

"Many people thought a housewife with five children had no business being in Selma at all. Who was looking after the children? Viola Gregg Liuzzo was no ordinary housewife. She was full of energy and independence, a natural 'trouble maker'. When she went to Selma she thought she was serving her family. Her family was mankind.

On the road to Selma today the wheel ruts gouged by Viola Liuzzo's Oldsmobile as it left the highway have been weathered in and grassed over. The four-strand barbed-wire fence, straddled by her car, has been repaired. But not everything is as it was. Someone comes along from time to time and places a small bouquet of field flowers beneath the barbed-wire."

Jack Mendelsohn, The Martyrs

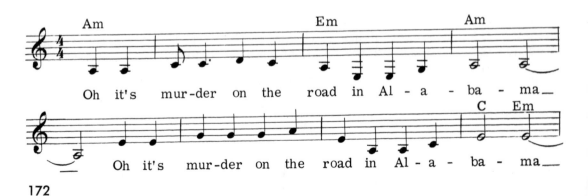

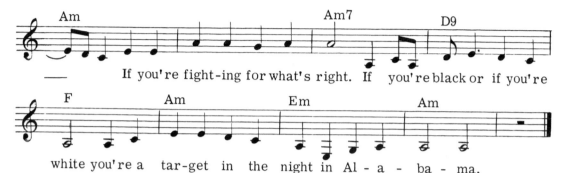

If you're fight-ing for what's right. If you're black or if you're
white you're a tar-get in the night in Al - a - ba - ma.

Oh it's murder on the road in Alabama.
Oh it's murder on the road in Alabama.
If you're fighting for what's right,
If you're black or if you're white
You're a target in the night in Alabama.

Oh we marched right by that spot in Alabama (2x)
Oh we marched right by that spot
Where the coward fired the shots
Where the Klansman fired the shots in Alabama.

Oh we know who is to blame in Alabama (2x)
She caught two bullets in the brain
Before we learned to say her name
And George Wallace is the shame of Alabama.

Deep within the sovereign state of Alabama (2x)
Deep within the sovereign state
There's a poison pit of hate,
And George Wallace is the heart of Alabama.

There's a man behind the guns of Alabama (2x)
There's a man behind the guns
Kills for hate, for fear, for fun,
And George Wallace is top gun of Alabama.

It was Jackson on the roads of Alabama
It was Reeb on the roads of Alabama,
William Moore's been dead and gone
But this killing still goes on
Now Liuzzo's on the road in Alabama.

There's a movement on the road in Alabama,
There's a movement on the road in Alabama,
Black man, white man, Christian, Jew
We've got to keep on marching through
Oh the tyrant days are few in Alabama.

It was murder on the road in Alabama. . . .

"The events in Selma demonstrated once more the traditional reluctance of politicians to move unless pressured by a set of disastrous events and an accompanying wave of indignation. President Johnson delivered finally a vigorous speech to a joint session of Congress on behalf of Negro rights, and asked for a strong voting bill to eliminate the subterfuges and schemes used by states to deprive Negroes of the right to vote.

"The bill was passed in late 1965."

Howard Zinn, SNCC: The New Abolitionists

"It is wrong -- deadly wrong -- to deny any of your fellow Americans the right to vote...We have already waited 100 years and more, and the time for waiting is gone...We Shall Overcome!"

President Johnson, presenting the
Voting Rights Bill

WE GOT
THE WHOLE WORLD SHAKIN'

Chicago and the North

It began when police tried to close a fire hydrant that had been opened by Negro youths for relief from 98-degree heat. Fighting broke out and for four days ghetto dwellers used rifles, rocks, bricks and "molotov cocktails" to inflict an untold amount of damage in Chicago's West Side. Finally 4,000 national guardsmen and 1,000 Chicago police armed with machine guns, teargas and orders to "shoot back -- shoot to kill" if they were fired upon put an end to the riot. Two Negroes were dead -- one a 14-year-old girl -- fifty others injured, and more than three hundred had been arrested. When it was over the Chicago black ghetto was about back where it started.

The Negro revolution has spread from the sprawling plantations of Mississippi and Alabama to the desolate slums and ghettos of the North. Like brush fire, riots have spread from city to city. In the summer of 1964 Harlem erupted into violence; in 1965 it was Watts, and in 1966 Chicago's West Side. These were not isolated events. This year the despair of Negro poverty, joblessness, slum housing, inadequate schools, crumbling family life exploded in major cities all across the country. There were out-breaks of violence in Cleveland, Omaha, Oakland, Lansing and Detroit, Brooklyn, Baltimore, San Francisco, Atlanta, Philadelphia and more. No U.S. city is safe from the explosiveness of Negro slums as long as they exist.

In face of this rising violent protest, the leaders of the non-violent movement have charted a course deep into the northern ghettos. Early in 1966 (before violence erupted there) Martin Luther King, Jr. moved his S.C.L.C. staff to Chicago to join forces with local groups in an effort to "End the Slums". As his aide Andrew Young put it, "We have got to deliver results -- non-violent results -- to protect the non-violent movement."

"Our primary objective in this first sustained northern movement will be to bring about the unconditional surrender of forces dedicated to the creation and maintenance of slums and ultimately to make slums a moral and financial liability upon the whole community. We do not hold that Chicago is alone among cities with a slum problem, but certainly we know that slum conditions here are the prototype of those chiefly responsible for the northern urban race problem.

"The Chicago problem is simply a matter of economic exploitation. Every condition exists simply because someone profits by its existence. In a slum, people do not receive comparable care and services for the amount of rent paid on a dwelling. Slum landlords find a lucrative return on a minimum investment. People are forced to purchase property at inflated real estate value. They pay taxes, but their children do not receive an equitable share of these taxes in educational, recreational and civic services. They may receive welfare, but the present system contributes to the breakdown of family life by making it difficult to obtain money if the father is in the houshold. A man or woman may leave the community and acquire professional training, skills or crafts, but seldom is he or she able to find employment opportunities commensurate with these skills. This means that in proportion to the labor, money and intellect which the slum pours into the community at large, only a small portion is received in return benefits. The Rev. James Bevel and our Chicago staff have come to see this as a system of internal colonialism.

"The city administration refuses to render adequate services to the Negro community, and the Federal Government has yet to initiate a creative attempt to deal with the problems of megalopolitan life and the results of the past three centuries of slavery and segregation on Negroes.

"We have chosen to concentrate on each and every one of these issues. We will work on a three phase assault:

"Phase one is based upon the principle that before people can be counted on to act, they must have a full understanding of the 'slum colony' and the resulting slum psychology, which lulls us into a somnolence of despair. The emphasis of this phase will be on education.

"During phase two demonstrations should be scheduled at specific points which reveal the agents of exploitation and paint a portrait of the evils which beset us in such a manner that it is clear the world over what makes up a slum and what it is that destroys the people who are forced to live in a slum.

"Phase three is a phase of massive action. As we begin to dramatize the situation, we will be led into forms of demonstration which will create the kind of coalition of conscience which is necessary to produce change in this country.

"Our objectives in this movement are federal, state and local. On the federal level we would hope to get the kind of comprehensive legislation which would meet the problems of slum life across the nation. At the state level, we should expect

the kinds of tax reforms, updating of building codes, open occupancy legislation and enforcement of existing statutes for the protection of our citizens. On the local level we would hope to create the kind of awareness in people that would make it impossible for them to be enslaved or abused and create for them the kind of democratic structures which will enable them to continually deal with the problems of slum life.

"We would also hope that from this would emerge several pilot projects and institutions which might be of some permanent significance."

Dr. Martin Luther King, Jr.
Winter 1966

"The Negro baby born in America today, regardless of the section or the state in which he is born, has about one-half as much chance of completing a high school as a white baby born in the same place, on the same day; one-third as much chance of completing college; one-third as much chance of becoming a professional man; twice as much chance of becoming unemployed; about one-seventh as much chance of earning $10,000 a year; a life expectancy which is seven years shorter, and the prospects of earning only half as much."

John F. Kennedy, June 11, 1963

I Don't Want To Be Lost In The Slums

Adaption: This Little Light of Mine Chicago Mvmt.

The rea-son I sing this song I don't wan-na be lost, The rea-son I sing this song, I don't wan-na be lost, the rea-son I sing this song, I don't wan-na be lost I don't wan-na be lost in the slum.

The reason I live this life,
  I don't want to be lost,
The reason I live this life,
  I don't want to be lost,
The reason I live this life,
  I don't want to be lost,
I don't want to be lost in the slums.

The reason I sing this song,
  I don't want to be lost...

The reason I join the movement...

The reason I march downtown...

The reason I go to jail...

The reason I sacrifice, Lord.

The reason I fight so hard...

Days of the slums are numbered....

Lost in the slums, Lord...

The reason I live this life...

Lead Poison On The Wall

The "End the Slums" Movement can claim its very own talented young composer, Jimmy Collier.

"Little children who are hungry all the time will chew on anything, so they've been eating paint that chipped off their walls. We found out about thirty kids died last year in Chicago from eating lead-based paint. Other children lost their eyesight or suffered brain damage. We got a group of teen-agers together -- kids from off the block -- and they began to cover the community, taking urine samples to spot danger in time and distributing information about lead poisoning. Then with rallies we made it a public issue.

Eventually Mayor Daley put three hundred people to work in the community on the problem, using war on poverty money. Earlier when this plan had been proposed, it was turned down."

Jimmy Collier

Lead poi - son on the wall,__ kills lit-tle guys__ and lit - tle__ dolls.__ It kills 'em big and it

kills 'em small,_ While we stand by and watch 'em fall,_ and the
land-lord does a-noth-ing to stop it all, That death on the
wall, that death on the wall. There's poi-son in the paint_
e-nough to make a lit-tle child_faint,_ e-nough to_ blind_
— his eye,_ e-nough to make him die. From that lead poi - son

Lead poison on the wall, kills little guys and little dolls,
It kills them big and it kills them small
While we stand by and watch them fall,
And the landlord does nothing to stop it all,
That death on the wall... death on the wall.

There's poison in the paint, enough to make a little child faint,
Enough to blind his eyes, enough to make him die, from the
Lead poison on the wall, kills little guys and little dolls,
Kills them big and it kills them small,
While we stand by and watch them fall,
And the landlord does nothing to stop it all,
That death on the wall.

There's plaster falling from the ceiling,
Plaster falling and plaster peeling,
Doesn't the landlord have any feeling?
Someone's responsible for all that killing, from that
Lead poison.... etc.

Urine samples and knockin' on doors
Label of paint in all of the stores,
Rally and action and you cannot ignore
There's still children dying so we've got do more, on that
Lead poison.... etc.

Rent Strike Blues

Words and Music: Jimmy Collier

"Yesterday a twelve month old baby died from a rat bite. The mother picked him up to feed him and the child's eye had been bitten out and he was dead. The landlord justified it by saying, 'well, they don't pick up their garbage. Anyway it was a nigger baby and they have a new one every year, so what does it matter?'

When the city found out about it, they sent some carpenters out to fix the rat-holes. They don't want to face the big problem, they just want to take care of individual incidents."

Jim Letherer, canvassing in Chicago

I got the rent strike, I got the rent strike blues
I got the rent strike, I got the rent strike blues,
Well if the landlord-y don't fix my building
Gonna have to try and move.

Well, I got rats on the ceiling, rats on the floor,
Rats all around, I can't stand it anymore
Going on a rent strike, got to end these blues
Well if the landlord-y don't fix my building
Gonna have to try and move.

I went next door to see my friend,
Landlord won't fix the building and the roaches let me in,
Going on a rent strike, got to end these blues.
Well, if the landlord-y don't fix my building,
Gonna have to try and move.

Well, no fire-escape have we got, no money has the landlord spent,
If he don't fix the building, ain't gonna get next month's rent
Got to go on a rent strike, got to end these blues.
If the landlord-y don't fix my building,
Gonna have to try and move.

Don't care what you do, don't care what you say
Everybody black and white 'titled to a decent place to stay,
Going on a rent strike, got to end these blues
If the landlord-y don't fix my building,
gonna have to try
Gonna have to try,
Landlord-y won't fix my building,
I ain't about to move!

Burn, Baby, Burn

"I made up this song while the riot in Watts was going on. I was searching for ways to try and express what I thought these fellows in Watts were trying to say by burning the town down.

We're trying to work with these same type fellows here in Chicago. Most of them think the Movement is kinda square. Their attitude is 'let's tear this town up.' They spend part of their time beating up white people and it's bad because this violence is becoming institutionalized. It's not their fault. It's the fault of the system, because you've got Negro guys growing up now who've never had good experiences with white people, and their families have never had good experiences with white people.

But now Orange* works out with some of them in karate and judo and he can lick 'em all, so they respect his ideas about non-violence.

And with this song, part way through, after they've sung the song and got out some of their hate and some of their vengeance, we try to put in our own pitch about using non-violence to change things. We say you've got to learn, baby, learn, and what you really want to do is build something rather than tear down."

Jimmy Collier

*James Orange - six feet, three inches, 280 lbs. - is a veteran of Alabama and other southern movements.

188

Middle of the summer, bitten by flies and fleas,
Sittin' in a crowded apartment, about a-hundred-and-ten degrees,
I went outside, the middle of the night
All I had was a match in my hand, but I wanted to fight,
So I said, burn, baby, burn
      Burn, baby, burn
      Nowhere to be, and-a no one to see,
      I said-a nowhere to turn
      Burn, baby, burn.

I called President Johnson on the phone,
The secretary said he wasn't there
I tried to get in touch with Mr. Humphrey
They couldn't find him anywhere.
I went into the courtroom, with my poor sad face
Didn't have no money, didn't have no lawyer
They wouldn't plead my case
So I said, Burn, baby, burn
      etc.

I really wanted a decent job, I really needed some scratch
  (I heard people talking about a dream, now, a dream that I couldn't catch
I really wanted to be somebody and all I had was a match
Couldn't get oil from Rockefeller's wells
Couldn't get diamonds from the mine
If I can't enjoy the American dream, won't be water but fire next time
So I said, Burn, baby, burn
      etc.

Walkin' around on the west side now, lookin' mean and mad
Deep down inside my heart, I'm feeling sorry and sad
Got a knife and a razor blade, everybody that I know is tough,
But when I tried to burn my way out of the ghetto,
I burned my own self up, when I said,
      Burn, baby, burn
      etc.

      Learn, baby, learn
      Learn, baby, learn
      You need a concern
      You've got money to earn
      You've got midnight oil to burn, baby, burn.

I really want a decent education, I really want a decent place to stay
I really want some decent clothes, now,
I really want a decent family
I really want a decent life like everybody else.....

People Get Ready

Original song: The Impressions
New words: Chicago Movement

"In addition to Jimmy Collier's songs, the 'End the Slums' movement has adapted many rhythm and blues songs. To the urban Negro of today, many of these songs provide an emotional release from the omnipresent suffering, while stimulating the will to struggle, serving them in much the same manner as the spirituals served their enslaved forefathers."

David Llorens, "New Birth in the Ghetto",
Sing Out! July 1966

Peo -ple get read - y, there's a train a -

com - ing, You don't need no tick - et, you just get on board. All you need is faith to hear the die - sel hum - ming, You don't need no tick - et____ You just thank the Lord.

People get ready, there's a train a-comin'
You don't need a ticket, just get on board.
All you need is faith to hear the diesel hummin'
You don't need no ticket, you just thank the Lord.

There ain't no room for the hopeless sinner
Who would hurt all mankind just to save his own (believe me now)
Have pity on those whose chances grow thinner
For there's no hiding place when the Movement comes.

(Believe me now)
People get ready for the train to Freedom
Pickin' up passengers from coast to coast.
Faith is the key, open the doors and board 'em
There's hope for all among this loving host.

Don't want no 'Toms' or any sorry Negroes
Comin' to me saying they won't go.
Everybody wants freedom
Everybody, this I know

People get ready for the train a-comin'
Don't need no ticket, you just get on board.
All you need is faith to hear the diesel hummin'
Don't need no luggage, you just thank the Lord.

Never Too Much Love

The Impressions - New Words: Chicago Movement

"There's a rock and roll group called the Impressions and we call them 'movement fellows' and we try to sing a lot of their songs. Songs like 'Keep on Pushin', 'I Been Trying', 'I'm So Proud', 'It's Gonna Be a Long, Long Winter', 'People Get Ready, There's a Train a-Comin', 'There's a Meeting Over Yonder' really speak to the situation a lot of us find ourselves in. One song that has really become kind of a favorite with us, especially when we got a lot of mean folks around, is 'Never Too Much Love'."

Jimmy Collier

Too much love,___ too much love,___ nev-er in this world will there be too much love.___ too much love.___ I like to drink whis-key, I like to drink wine, I'd like to have some now, but I just ain't got the time. I got-ta fight for my free - dom, got-ta fight for it now,___ Join___ ___ with the move-ment and we'll show you how.___

CHORUS:
Too much love, too much love,
Never in this world will there be too
    much love.
Too much love, too much love
Never in this world will there be too
    much love.

I like to drink whisky, I like to drink
    wine,
I'd like to have some now, but I just
    ain't got the time.
I gotta fight for my freedom and
    fight for it now
Join with the movement and we'll
    show you how.

CHORUS

I don't know but I think I'm right
Folks in heaven both black and white
I don't know but I've been told,
Folks in heaven won't tell me where
    to go.

CHORUS

*"Now one thing we try to do with this song is to get people
to make up verses. You'd be surprised what kind of verses
come from people who don't consider themselves songwriters
or singers ... Some people don't even consider themselves
people."*

Too much hate, too much hate
Always in this world there is too
    much hate.
Too much war, too much war,
Always in this world there is too
    much war.

War is sad, war is long
Everybody knows that war is wrong,
People tired, people sore,
People just want to end the war.

People in Mississippi thrown off
    their land
Even the government won't give a
    hand.
But the Movement stays on and on
People are living on hope and a song.

If religion were a thing that money
    could buy
The rich would live and the poor would
    die,
But I thank my god it is not so
Both the rich and poor together must
    go.

Some people are good, some people
    are bad,
Some people are happy, some people
    are sad,
Some people are black, some people
    are white,
But we're all together in the human
    plight.

They say the Movement is a non-
    violent thing
Led by people like Martin Luther
    King,
I want my freedom , and I want it
    now
Join with us and we will show you
    how.

Gonna Be A Meetin'
Over Yonder

The Impressions - New words: Chicago Movement

We in the East Garfield Park Community Organization have been accused of inciting race hatred and attacking white leaders without just cause. This is a big fat lie. We have never talked race hatred, but we have attacked the practices of "so-called" white leaders and with plenty of just cause. They bury their heads in the sand and ignore the Negro in the slums until he speaks out against the evils that exist in this community. Some Uncle Toms want the Negro in the slums to stay in these deplorable conditions so that they can continue to draw their fat checks from the man downtown and ride around in big fine cars and wear fancy clothes. No matter what boss and his boys say I still don't like:

1. *SLUMS*
2. *OVERCROWDED SCHOOLS*
3. *SLAVE WAGES*
4. *A. D. C. **
5. *RATS & ROACHES*
6. *FILTHY ALLEYS*
7. *POLICE HARRASSMENT*
8. *ABSENTEE POLITICANS*
9. *BLACK LACKEYS*
10. *UNINFORMED PEOPLE WHO CRITICIZE CONCERNED NEIGHBORHOOD ORGANIZATIONS*

(* aid to dependent children)

If you want to know what we are doing, come to our next meeting. All civil rights meetings are open to everybody. See you any Wednesday at 7:30 P. M.

Leo McCord - Citizen of East Garfield
Member of Organization
P. S. FREEDOM

Children, are you ready?
Gonna be a meetin' over yonder.
Children, are you ready?
Gonna be a meetin' over yonder.
All the boys and the girls gonna
  be there,
And you know the weak and strong
  gonna be there,
Children, are you ready?
Gonna be a meetin' over yonder.

Don't forget to be there
Be at the meetin' over yonder.
Dr. King's gonna be there
Be at the meetin' over yonder.
Don't you know weak and strong
  gonna be there,
The meek and the bold gonna
  be there
Children, are you ready?
Gonna be a meetin' over yonder.

(Keep on pushin' now)

Repeat first verse.

"Young people have made every movement -- from Nashville to Selma..."

"A considerable percentage of the 100,000 unemployed Negroes in Chicago are young men between the ages of 16 and 25. Many of these are in gangs or are drifting idly from corner to corner. This group must be mobilized into an action unit. They must be organized in their own behalf with the focus on meaningful employment and training opportunities through which they might achieve active participation in our society."

Martin Luther King, Jr.

"We have a program of taking teen-agers out to the country on week-ends. We took a bunch of kids up one week-end -- these were supposed to be mean and vicious kids, the gangs you hear about. When we got there they asked us the rules. We had a little session about Negro history, told them about Nat Turner and a few of those folks, and you could see the pride come out on their faces. Then they asked again, what are the rules? So we told them, 'Well, we're going out for coffee and when we come back, you tell us the rules.' We came back in a half hour and they gave us wine bottles, brass knuckles, a few zip guns, knives. They said, 'O.K. first rule is no fighting.'

"The next morning, the kids had a big breakfast. We didn't push them, we let them do what they wanted with their time. So after breakfast they said, 'O.K. we're gonna run for awhile.' This place is a farm with hills. One kid looked out and said, 'Hey man, where's all the houses where all the folks live?' These kids from the ghetto just had no concept that people didn't live crammed up together everywhere.

They started running, and it was beautiful. They ran for an hour and a half -- up and down hills. They'd never had a chance to do that before.

"These kids come back from a session of talking about what's keeping them down, and they lose a little respect for their parents. They want to know how come they never fought the oppression. We don't try to tell them what they can do. We just help them understand what the problems are and then we ask them what they think they can do."

Jim Letherer

198

Freedom Now

New words: Chicago Movement

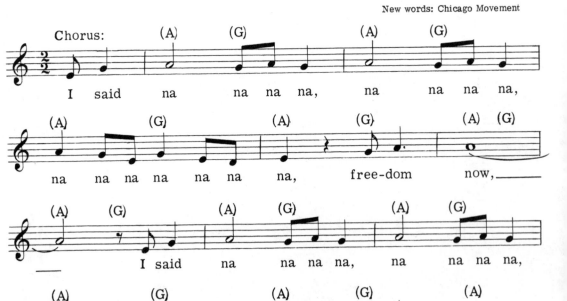

Chorus:

I said na na na na, na na na na,
na na na na na na na, free-dom now,_____

I said na na na na, na na na na,
na na na na na na na, free-dom now._____

Verse:

Do you want your free-dom? Oh yes. Do you want your free-dom? Oh yes. Do you want your free-dom? Oh yes. Will you fight for your free-dom? Oh yes.__

I said now - na na na na na na na na na na na na na na Freedom now!
I said now - na na na na na na na na na na na na na na Freedom now!

LEAD	GROUP
Do you want your freedom?	oh yes
Do you want your freedom?	oh yes
Do you want your freedom?	oh yes
Do you want your freedom?	oh yes
Come on and sing now	oh yes
Sing for your freedom	oh yes
Do you want your freedom?	oh yes
Do you want your freedom?	oh yes

I said now - na na na na na na na na na na na na na na Freedom now!
I said now - na na na na na na na na na na na na na na Freedom now!

Do you want a job?	oh yes
Then join the movement	oh yes
Do you want education?	oh yes
Then come with me	oh yes
Do you want a home?	oh yes
We're gonna march, children	oh yes
We're gonna end the slums	oh yes
With urban renewal	oh yes
With urban renewal	oh yes
Urban renewal	oh yes
We're gonna stamp out the slums	oh yes

We're gonna do it now - na na na na na na na na na na Freedom now!
We're gonna do it now - na na na na na na na na na na Freedom now!

We Got The Whole World Shakin'

Sam Cooke - New words: Chicago Movement

This first major experiment with non-violent protest in the North seemed only to inflame whites to riotous anger. As Dr. King and his staff led march after march into working-class white neighborhoods this summer (1966) they were met again and again with a barrage of bricks, bottles and fire-crackers, confederate flags and chants of "nigger, nigger, nigger". On one occasion their cars were overturned and set afire. Dr. King was moved finally to announce that he had never seen such hate -- not in Mississippi or Alabama -- as he saw in Chicago. "We have marched all over the South, but never before have I seen so many people with hatred in their faces and violence in their hearts." He was hit on the head with a rock and jeered and cursed by middle-class whites as he and his marchers protested the imprisonment of a million Chicago Negroes in wretched ghettos and asked for equal access to housing.

Segregationists in the South have predicted for years that when the movement came North people would oppose racial equality as bitterly as they did in the South -- only with more humbug and hypocrisy. Now the time had come and the dire predictions were coming true. When the "race problem" crossed the Mason-Dixon line and encamped in the neighborhoods of the North the result was hysteria and violence in Chicago and other cities -- and retreat and compromise in Congress.

While it had been relatively easy to design and support legislation striking down discrimination in the South, it became impossible to pass a strong bill aimed at open housing in the North.

Whole world shak - in' now, Whole world shak - in' now,

Oh,_____ Whole world shak-in' now whole world.

We got the whole world shakin', now
Something must be going on.
We got the whole world shakin'
Something must be going on, all
  right.
We got to keep on pushin'
Just a little way to go, all right.
We got the whole city brimmin'
A movement's going on, all right.
We got the whole city brimmin', now
Got a movement going on.
Oh now, keep on pushin'
Just a little way to go, all right.

CHORUS:
Whole world shakin', whole world
  shakin', whole world shakin' (8x)
Oh........oh, whole world shakin',
  whole world shakin'

We got the whole world shakin', Dr.
  King is on his way.
Oh, the whole world shakin', Dr.
  King is on his way, all right
We got to keep on pushin', we might
  get our freedom today, all right.

CHORUS

The Chicago Movement vowed to press on in spite of the violence. They temporarily called off the demonstrations when they were able to come up with a ten-point agreement with top civic and business leaders in Chicago. It is a far cry from the "open city' which King and his movement strive for, but it provided a much needed rest from the marches which provoked such violence.

It remains to be seen just how much this movement -- or any northern non-violent movement -- can accomplish. So far the main thing it has done is to expose the racism of a northern city in a highly visible way and to force the entire country to recognize it. The southern campaigns begin to seem almost easy compared to the difficulty of the urban north with its complex tangle of slum-housing, chronic joblessness, poor schools and deteriorating family life. The frustrations and disappointments of Negroes caught in the ghettos of a rich nation are more easily mobilized by riots and angry protest than by the reasoned words of a Martin Luther King.

As Dr. King himself explains:

"Surrounded by an historic prosperity in the white society, taunted by empty promises, humiliated and deprived by the filth and decay of his ghetto home, some Negroes find violence alluring. They have convinced themselves that it is the only method to shock and pressure the white majority to come to terms with an evil of staggering proportions.

"I cannot question that these brutal facts of Negro life exist. I differ with the extremist solution. Our demonstrations, boycotts, civil disobedience, and political action in Negro-white unity won significant victories. In our judgement it remains the method that can succeed. In this conviction the vast majority of Negroes are still with us. In the face of cries of 'Black Power' we helped to summon 60,000 Negroes in the sweltering slums of Chicago to assemble non-violently for protest -- and they responded magnificently.

"The burden now shifts to the municipal, state, and Federal authorities and all men in seats of power. If they continue to use our non-violence as a cushion for complacency, the wrath of those suffering a long train of abuses will rise. The consequence can well be unmanageable and persisting social disaster and moral disaster.

"Negroes can still march down the path of non-violence and interracial amity if white America will meet them with honest determination to rid society of its inequality and inhumanity."

> Martin Luther King, Jr.
> "Black Power", The Progressive, 1966

Keep On Pushing

The Impressions

"Somehow we've got to break down slum conditions and what they do to people. Rats and roaches, overcrowdedness, lack of concern by the landlord -- these things destroy people's motivation, their hope and their vision. The conditions have to be changed and the hold that they have on people must be broken. That's what our Movement is. We say 'End the Slums', but we mean to give life to people who have died because of what the system has done to them. "

Jimmy Collier

Keep on_ push - ing, Keep on_ push - ing,

I've got to keep on_ push-ing, mm_____ I

can't stop now. Move up a lit - tle

high - er, Some way, some how,

'Cause I've got my strength and it don't make

sense, Not to keep on_ push - ing_

Hal - le - lu - jah_ Hal - le-

lu - jah,　　　　　　Keep on＿　push - ing.

Keep on pushing... keep on pushing
I got to keep on pushing, I can't
stop now
Move up a little higher, someway,
somehow
'Cause I've got my strength, and it
don't make sense
Not to keep on pushing.

Hallellujah, hallellujah,
Keep on pushing.

Now maybe someday I'll reach that
higher goal,
I know I can make it, with just a
little bit of soul.
'Cause I've got my strength, and it
don't make sense
Not to keep on pushing.

Look-a, look-a yonder, what's
that I see
A great big stone standing there
ahead of me.
But I've got my strength, and it don't
make sense
Not to keep on pushing.

Hallellujah, hallellujah,
Keep on pushing.

Keep on pushing.... keep on pushing...

PREFACE TO EPILOGUE

As Dr. King and others labor on in a spirit of non-violence and interracial unity, another approach to social change is gaining ground. Referred to commonly as "the new mood" or the "black power" drive, it is being given form by SNCC and CORE. As SNCC's head Stokely Carmichael has defined it, Black Power is a means for the black poor to get together, define their needs and put people in power to achieve them It is the massed political, economic, emotional and physical strength of the black community exercised in the interest of the total black community -- not in the interest of the Negro middle-class or the individual designated to represent the black community -- but in the interest of its largest part, the overwhelming majority of poor sharecroppers and slum-dwellers of the South and the North. An important part of the new mood is a growing cynicism about non-violence.

With this in mind, we asked Julius Lester -- a writer and photographer for SNCC -- to write an epilogue to this book; for as he would have it, an epilogue to the entire period from 1960 to 1966. For in his opinion the time of freedom singing is past. His words are angry and for many they will be hard to take, but they are important if one is to understand the new mood.

We preface the epilogue with some relevant thoughts from Stokely Carmichael:

> "One of the tragedies of the struggle against racism is that up to **now** there has been no national organization which could speak to the growing militancy of young black people in the urban ghetto. There has been only a civil rights movement, whose tone of voice was adapted to an audience of liberal whites. It served as a sort of buffer zone between them and angry young blacks. None of its so-called leaders could go into a rioting community and be listened to. In a sense, I blame ourselves -- together with the mass media -- for what has happened in Watts, Harlem, Chicago, Cleveland, Omaha. Each time the people in those cities saw Martin Luther King get slapped, they became angry; when they saw four little black girls bombed to death, they were angrier; and when nothing h a p p e n e d, they were steaming. We had nothing to offer that they could see, except to go out and be beaten again. We helped to build their frustration.
>
> For too many years, black Americans marched and had their heads broken and got shot. They were saying to the country, "Look, you guys

we are only going to do what we are supposed to do -- why do you beat us up, why don't you give us what we ask, why don't you straighten yourselves out?" After years of this, we are at almost the same point -- because we demonstrated from a position of weakness. We cannot be expected any longer to march and have our heads broken in order to say to whites; come on, you're nice guys. For you are not nice guys. We have found you out.

An organization which claims to speak for the needs of a community -- as does the Student Nonviolent Coordinating Committee -- must speak in the tone of that community, not at somebody else's buffer zone. This is the significance of black power as a slogan. For once, black people are going to use the words they want to use -- not just the words whites want to hear."

Stokely Carmichael, "What We Want", _The N.Y. Review of Books_
9-22-66

G.C. & C.C.

THE MOVEMENT'S MOVING ON:
The New Mood

The world of the black American is different from that of the white American. This difference comes not only from the segregation imposed on the black, but it also comes from the way of life he has evolved for himself under these conditions. Yet, America has always been uneasy with this separate world in its midst. Feeling most comfortable when the black man emulates the ways and manners of white Americans, America has, at the same time, been stolidly unwilling to let the black man be assimilated into the mainstream.

With its goal of assimilation on the basis of equality, the civil rights movement was once the great hope of black men and liberal whites. In 1960 and 1961 Negroes felt that if only Americans knew the wrongs and sufferings they had to endure, these wrongs would be righted and all would be well. If Americans saw well-dressed, well-mannered, clean Negroes on their television screen not retaliating to being beaten by white Southerners, they would not sit back and no dothing. Amor vincit omnia! and the Reverend Dr. Martin Luther King, Jr., was the knight going forth to prove to the father that he was worthy of becoming a member of the family. But there was something wrong with this attitude and young Negroes began to feel ...easy. Was this not another form of the bowing and scraping their grandparents had had to do to get what they wanted? Were they not acting once again as the white man wanted and expected them to? And why should they have to be brutalized, physically and spiritually, for what every other American had at birth? But these were only timid questions in the mind for which no answer was waited. You simply put your body in the struggle and that meant entering the church in Albany, Danville, Birmingham, Greenwood, Nashville, or wherever you were, entering the church and listening to prayers, short semons on your courage and the cause you were fighting, singing freedom songs---Ain't Gon' Let Nobody Turn Me Round, Turn Me Round, Turn Me Round and you would name names, the sheriff's, the Mayor's,

the Governor's and whoever else you held responsible for the conditions and--- always at the end---We Shall Overcome with arms crossed, holding the hands of the person next to you and swaying gently from side to side, We Shall Overcome Someday someday but not today because you knew as you walked out of the church, two abreast, and started marching toward town that no matter how many times you sang about not letting anybody turn you around red-necks and po' white trash from four counties and some from across the state line were waiting with guns, tire chains, baseball bats, rocks, sticks, clubs and bottles, waiting as you turned the corner singing about This Little Light of Mine and how you were going to let it shine as that cop's billy club went upside your head shine shine shining as you fell to the pavement with someone's knee crashing into your stomach and somone's foot into your back until a cop dragged you away, threw you into the paddy wagon and off to the jail you and the others went, singing I Ain't Scared of Your Jail 'Cause I Want My Freedom. Freedom! Freedom! Was it a place somewhere between Atlanta and Birmingham and you kept on missing it everytime you drove that way? It was a street in Itta Bena, Mississippi. Ain't that a bitch? Freedom Street! Ran right by the railroad tracks in the Negro part of town and Love Street ran right into it. Freedom and Love. It would be nice to have a house right on that corner. Freedom and Love. But from what you'd heard it was just a street in Itta Bena. Maybe it was a person---Freedom. Somebody sitting on a porch somewhere. You wondered what he looked like as you sat in the jail cell with ten, twenty, thirty others and one toilet that wouldn't flush and one useless window stopped up with bars. If it was summer the jailer would turn the heat on and it was winter he'd turn it off and take the mattresses and you'd sing Freedom Songs (your brother sent you a note and said you looked real good on the six o'clock news on TV walking down the street singing) until the guard came and said Shut Up All That Damn Noise and you'd sing louder and he'd take one of you out at a time and everybody'd get quiet and listen to the screams and cries from the floor above and then that one would come back, bleeding, and you'd sing again because if one went to jail, all went; if one got a beating, all got beatings and then that night or the next day or the day after the people would've got up enough money to bail you out and you'd go back to the church and march again and your brother would see you on the six o'clock news for thirty seconds between the stock market report and Jackie Kennedy flying to Switzerland with her children for skiing lessons.

But a response did begin to come from the nation. All across the North young white kids held sympathy demonstrations and then with the Freedom Rides in 1961 whites came South to go to jail with Negroes --- for Freedom. Those who came said integration was their fight, too, because they could never be whole men, either, in a segregated society. Some whites stayed after the Freedom Rides and moved into Negro communities to live and to work.

At that time there was a split between activists in The Movement. Some felt that more and more demonstrations were needed, while others felt that the effect of demonstrations was limited. Power was what was needed and power came through having a say in the system. That came through the ballot. Once you had some say in government, you could have a say about jobs. After all, what was the point of desegregating a lunch counter if you didn't have the money to buy a hamburger?

So began the slow tedious work of going into a town, finding someone who wouldn't be afraid to have a civil rights worker living in his house and would help the worker become known in the community. The civil rights worker had to find a minister courageous enough to let his church be used for a mass meeting and then he had to go around the community asking people to come out to the meeting. At the mass meeting there was usually hymn singing and a prayer service first. Then the minister would make a few remarks before introducing the civil rights worker, who by that time, if he were a veteran, would've been through the sit-ins, the Freedom Rides, five or six different jails and a lot of hungry days. He had dropped out of college, or quit his job if he had never been to college to become a full-time organize for SNCC. His job was simple: organize the community to march down to the courthouse to register to vote. In small Mississippi towns, though, he didn't even think of organizing the community. He would feel good if he could convince five people to go. If five went and if the inevitable happened (violence, arrests), he had a good chance of organizing the community. It was not important at that time if one name was put on the voter registration rolls. The most important thing was to get the people organized.

It was out of Mississippi that one of the most important concepts of "the move-ment" came. Let the people lead themselves. SNCC field workers provided the impetus to a community, but let the community choose its leaders from its own ranks. To symbolize their new feeling, they began wearing denim work overalls, saying that they, too, were one of the community, that community of the poor. They rejected the idea of the 'talented tenth,' who would come out of the colleges to lead. There would be no 'talented tenth.' Only the community.

There were still demonstrations, but now they were not aimed as much at public accomodations, the most obvious symbols of oppression. The picket line around the courthouse, the symbol of the seat of power, was the new target. The immediate result was the same. Heads that had been beaten before were beaten again. Heads that had never been beaten were beaten. New bloody heads were on the six o'clock news alongside ones that still had scabs from the last head-whipping session. If you were a civil rights worker in Mississippi you learned many things quickly. Don't sleep by windows if possible. Don't answer a knock at the door in the middle of the night unless your caller showed you nothing less than his birth certificate. If you're on the highway at night you learned to drive as if you were training to be an astronaut. If a car was following you while you were doing ninety and it didn't sound a siren, it was safe to assume that the people in that car were not delivering a telegram. One SNCC worker, an ex-stock car driver, learned how to make a U-turn while doing ninety. (Take your hands off the wheel and pull the hand-brake. The car will spin around. Release the hand-brake and accelerate.) Each organizer had his own little techniques for staying alive. Non-violence might do something to the moral conscience of a nation, but a bullet didn't have morals and it was beginning to occur to more and more organizers that white folks had plenty more bullets than they did conscience.

How naive, how idealistic they were then. They had honestly believed that once white people knew what segregation did, it would be abolished. But why shouldn't they have believed it? They had been fed the American Dream, too. They believed in Coca Cola and the American Government. "I dreamed I got my Free-dom in Maidenform bra." They were in the Pepsi Generation, believing that the F.B.I. was God's personal emissary to uphold good and punish evil.

That was before the countless demonstrations where the F.B.I. took notes standing next to cracker cops while they were wiping nigger blood off their billy clubs and checking the batteries on their cattle-prods. That was before the promises of the Justice Department began to sound like the teasing of a virgin who never gets down to where it's at. Sure, it was nice to see that picture of Bobby Kennedy up all night at his desk during the Freedom Rides. He looked almost like a civil rights worker drinking coffee with his shoes off, but it took those Freedom Rides to make the ICC rule out segregated seating on interstate bus travel. It was Birmingham, '63 that finally forced the Image of Youth and Liberality, John Kennedy, into proposing a Civil Rights Bill, which was then almost immediately compromised into ineffectiveness when the Brother of the Image, Bobby the K, appeared before the Seante Judiciary Committee. They didn't like the idea of the March on Washington, but managed to turn it into a Kennedy victory by finally endorsing it as being in the American tradition, whatever that means. After the march the American Monarch had the Big Six Negro Leaders over to the White House for tea and cookies and to chat with Jackie about the Riviera in the winter (It's a whole lot better than the Delta I hear). The Monarch, his face rugged from the spray of the wind-swept Atlantic, as thousands of eulogies have proclaimed since his swift demise, stood there smiling, feeling pretty good because all the liquor stores and bars in Washington had been closed for the day so there was no danger of a bunch of niggers getting a hold of some fire-water and forgetting

216

that they weren't in Harlem, Buttermild Bottom and all those other weird-named places niggers pick to live in. (The order forbidding the sale of alcoholic beverages is one of the biggest insults Negroes have ever had hurled at them. It would've been been much easier to take if it had simply been said The Great White Father can't trust his pickaninnies if the bars and liquor stores are left open.) Jack could also stand there and smile because John Lewis of SNCC had had his speech consored by the more 'responsible' leaders, who threatened to withdraw from the March. Even censored, Lewis' speech raised pertinent questions---questions that had been on the minds of many, those not leaders, those not responsible. "The party of Kennedy is also the party of Eastland. The party of Javits is also the party of Goldwater. Where is our party?'' but Jack could smile, because John Lewis had deleted from his speech the most pertinent question of all "I want to know---which side is the Federal Government on?''

A lot of people wanted to know that, particularly after Lyndon Baines Johnson became President of the United States in a split second one Friday afternoon. When he asked for the nation's help and God's in that cracker drawl Negroes began pulling out road maps, train schedules and brushing up on their Spanish. A lot of them had always wanted to see what Mexico was like anyway and it looked as if the time to do that thing was near.

But big Lyndon, despite his beagle hounds and daughters, fooled everybody. Not only did he strengthen the civil rights bill and support it fully, he started giving Martin Luther King competition as to who was going to lead "the movement,'' King lost.

With the push for the civil rights bill in Congress there began talk of a white backlash in the '64 elections. It seemed that whites were getting a little tired of picking up the papers and seeing niggers all over the front page. Even if they were getting their heads kicked in half the time, four years of seeing that was about enough. The average white person didn't know what niggers wanted and didn't much care. By now they should've gotten whatever the hell it was they said they didn't have and if they hadn't got it by now, they either didn't deserve it or didn't need it.

What was really bothering northern whites, however, was the fact that The Movement had come North. De Facto Segregation and De Facto Housing were new phrases, meaning No Niggers Allowed in This School and You Damn Well Better Believe No Niggers Allowed in This Neighborhood. If you believed the liberal press, though, it wasn't as serious a problem as the one down South, because in the North segregation wasn't deliberate. It just sorta happened that way. Many Negroes never found out exactly what De Facto meant, but they assumed it was the De Facto and not segregation they ran up against when they couldn't find an apartment to rent outside Harlem. Soon, though, the mask fell from the North's face. In New York it happened when CORE threatened a stall-in on all of the city's expressways the morning of the Wrold's Fair opening. The threat alone was enough to make over three-fourths of the people who drove to work leave their cars in the garage and take the train or simply call in sick. The threat alone was enough to make New York's liberal newspapers read as if they had come out of the editorial room of the Birmingham News and the radio and television commentators sounded as if they had acquired southern accents over night. A few months later an organization arose in New York which called itself SPONGE --- Society for the Prevention of Negroes Getting Everything. It was difficult to speak any longer of a North and a South. As Malcolm X once said, everything south of the Canadian border was South. There was only up South and down South now, and you found "crackers'' both places.

While the North was being shocked into realizing that there were Negroes in its midst, the South was sympathizing with the assault that Mississippi was about to suffer. Almost a thousand white students were going into the state in June, 1964, to work in Freedom schools, community centers and to register people in the Mississippi Freedom Democratic Party, a political party organized that winter which was going to challenge the state Democratic organization at the Democratic Convention in August.

The Mississippi Summer Project was the apex of white participation in The Movement and marked the end of that participation. Within SNCC there had been widespread oppositiin to the idea. Many felt that it was admitting that Negroes couldn't do the job alone. Others felt that it would destroy everything which they had accomplished. White, no matter how well-meaning, could not relate to the Negro community. A Negro would follow a white person to the courthouse, not because he'd been convinced he should register to vote, but simply because he had been trained to say Yes to whatever a white person wanted. Others felt, however, that if they were to ever expose Mississippi's racism to America, it would only be through using whites. After all, SNCC had repeatedly informed the press of the five Negroes killed that year in Mississippi because of their involvement with The Movement. The press had refused to print or investigate the information. Put a thousand white kids in Mississippi and the press would watch everything and print it. And who could tell? Maybe one of them white boys would get himself killed and really bring some publicity. A few said it. Most thought it. It happened.

The murders of Goodman, Schwerner and Chaney stunned the nation. Whites were shocked. Negroes were hurt and angry. Rita Schwerner, wife of one of the murdered men, reflected the feelings of Negroes when she commented that if James Chaney had been killed alone, no one would've cared. This was made even more evident even the following year when Jimmie Lee Jackson's murder in Alabama evoked little reaction from whites, but the murder of Rev. James Reeb brough thousands of whites to Harlem on a march protesting his slaying.

The Mississippi Summer Project accomplished its purpose; the press came to Mississippi. The feature stories it wrote usually went something like, "Blop-blop is a blue-eyed blonde from Diamond, Junction-on-the-Hudson, New York. She's a twenty-year-old junior at Radcliffe majoring in Oriental metaphysics and its relationship to the quantum theory when the sun is in Saggitarius. This summer she's living with a Negro family in Fatback, Mississippi who has never heard of the quantum theory, etc., etc., etc." All summer the articles came about white boys and white girls living with poor Negroes in Mississippi. It didn't escape the attention of Negroes that seemingly no one cared about the Negro civil rights workers who had been living and working in Mississippi for the previous three years. Didn't anyone care about Willie Peacock, born and raised on a Mississippi plantation, who couldn't go back to his home town because he was an organizer for SNCC and the white people would kill him if he went to see his mother? Apparently not.

Mississippi was taken out of the beadlines in July, however, when Harlem held its own Summer Project to protest the murder of a 13-year-old boy by a policeman. Summer Projects, northern style, usually involve filling a Coke bottle with gasoline, stuffing a rag down the neck and lighting it. Things Go Better with Coke! Harlem, Bedord-Stuyvesant, Rochester and Chicago sent Coke after Coke after Coke that summer with the grandaddy of them all, Watts, to come the following summer.

If the press had ever screamed as loudly for an end to segregation and discrimination as it screamed for law and order, segregation would be a vague memory today. Somehow, though, law and order becomes all important only when Negroes take to the streets and burn down a few of the white man's stores. Law and order is never so important to the p r e s s when police are whuppin' nigger's heads on the week-end. It slowly began to dawn on Negroes that whites didn't care so much about helping them get their freedom as they did about law and order. "Law and order must prevail" has become the cliche of the sixties. Law and order has always prevailed --- upside the black man's head at every available opportunity.

The system was breaking down, but it was breaking in ways few had foreseen and fewer understood. The walls of segregation and discrimination were not crumbling and giving way to flowers of love and brotherhood. The walls were crumbling, but only to reveal a gigantic castle with walls ten times thicker than the walls of segregation. The castle was painted a brilliant white and lettered in bright red were the words Racism. What it meant to the Negro was simple. The white man only wanted you to have what he wanted you to have and you couldn't get it any other way except the way he said you could get it. Racism. It was the attitude that closed the bars and liquor stores on the day of the March. It was the attitude which made newspapers and Government officials, even Big Lyndon Himself, say, "that if Negroes went about things in the wrong way they would lose the friends they already had." It was the attitude that made the press continue to call Muhhamud Ali, Cassius Clay even though that was no longer his name. But the movement was moving. It was no longer a Friendship Contest. It was becoming a War of Liberation.

More than any other person Malcolm X was responsible for the new militancy that entered The Movement in 1965. Malcolm X said aloud those things which Negroes had been saying among themselves. He even said those things Negroes had been afraid to say to each other. His clear, umcomplicated words cut through the chains on black minds like a giant blow-torch. His words were not spoken for the benefit of the press. He was not concerned with stirring the moral conscience of America, because he knew --- America had no moral conscience. He spoke directly and eloquently to black men, analyzing their situation, their predicament, events as they happened, explaining what it all meant for a black man in America.

America's reaction to what the Negro considered just demands was a disillusioning experience. Where whites could try to attain the American Dream, Negroes always had had to dream themselves attaining The Dream. But The Dream was beginning to look like a nightmare and Negroes didn't have to dream themselves a nightmare. They'd been living one a long time. They had hopes that America would respond to their needs and America had equivocated. Integration had once been an unquestioned goal that would be the proudest moment for Negro America. Now it was beginning to be questioned.

The New York school boycotts of 1964 pointed this up. Integration to the New York City Board of Education meant busing Negro children to white schools. This merely said to Negroes that whites were saying Negroes had nothing to offer. Integration has always been presented as a Godsend for Negroes and something to be endured for whites. When the Board of Ed decided to bus white children to Negro schools the following year, the reaction was strangely similiar to that of New Orleans and Little Rock. Today, whites in Chicato and New York chant at Negro demonstrators, "I wish I was an Alabama deputy, so I could kill a nigger legally."

When it became more and more apparent that integration was only designed to uplift Negroes and improve their lot, Negroes began wondering whose lot actually needed improving. Maybe the white folks weren't as well-educated and cultured as they thought they were. Thus, Negroes began cutting a path toward learning who they were.

Of the minority groups in this country, the Negro is the only one lacking a language of his own. This is significant in that this has made it difficult for him to have a clear concept of himself as a Negro. It has made him more susceptible to the American lie of assimilation than the Puerto Rican, Italian or Jew who can remove himself from America with one sentence in his native language. Despite the assimilation lie, America is not a melting pot. It is a nation of national minorities, each living in a well-defined geographical area and retaining enough of the customs of the native land to maintain an identity other than that of an American. The Negro has two native lands: America and Africa. Both have deliberately been denied him.

Identity has always been the key problem for Negroes. Many avoid their blackness as much as possible by trying to become assimilated. They remove all traces of blackness from their lives. Their gestures, speech, habits, cuisine, walk, everything becomes as American Dream as possible. Generally, they are the 'responsible leaders', the middle class, the undercover, button-down collar Uncle Toms, who front for the white man at a time of racial crisis, reassuring the nation that "responsible Negroes deplore the violence and looting and we ask that law and order be allowed to prevail." A small minority avoid the crux of their blackness by going to another extreme. They identify completely with Africa. Some go to the extent of wearing African clothes and speaking Swahili. They, however, are only unconsciously admitting that the white man is right when he says, Negroes don't have a thing of their own.

For other Negroes the question of identity is only now being solved by the realization of those things that are their's. Negroes do have a language of their own. The words may be English, but the way a Negro puts them together and the meaning that he gives them creates a new language. He has another language, too, and that language is rhythm. It is obvious in music, but it is also expressed in the way he walks and the way he talks. There is a music and rhythm to the way he dresses and the way he cooks. This has been recognized by Negroes for some time now. "Soul" is how these things peculiarly black are recognized by black men in America. In Africa they speak Negritude. It is the same. The recognition of those things uniquely theirs which separate them from the white man. "Soul" and Negritude become even more precious when it is remembered that the white man in America systematically tried to destroy every vestige of racial identity through slavery and slavery's little brother, segregation. It is a testament to the power of "Soul" that it not only survived, but thrived.

Now the Negro is beginning to study his past, to learn those things that have been lost, to recreate what the white man destroyed in him and to destroy that which the white man put in its stead. He has stopped being a Negro and has become a black man in recognition of his new identity, his real identity. 'negro' is an American invention which shut him off from those of the same color in Africa. He recognizes now that part of himself is in Africa. Some feel this in a deeply personal way, as did Mrs. Fannie Lou Hamer who cried when she was in Africa, because she knew she had relatives there and she would never be able to know them. Her past would always be partially closed.

Many things that have happened in the past six years have had little or no meaning for most whites, but have had vital meaning for Negroes. Wasn't it only a month after the March on Washington that four children were killed in a church bombing in Birmingham? Whites could feel morally outraged, but they couldn't know the futility, despair and anger that swept through the The Nation within a nation --- Black America. There were limits to how much one people could endure and Birmingham Sunday possibly marked that limit. The enemy was not a system. It was an inhuman fiend who never slept, who never rested and no one would stop him. Those Northern protest rallies where Freedom Songs were sung and speeches speeched and applause applauded and afterwards telegrams and letters sent to the President and Congress --- they began to look more and more like moral exercises. See, my hands are clean. I do not condone such a foul deed, they said, going back to their magazine and newspapers, feeling purged because they had made their moral witness.

What was needed that Sunday was ol' John Brown to come riding into Birmingham as he had ridden into Lawrence, Kansas, burning every building that stood and killing every man, woman and child that ran from his onslaught. Killing, killing, killing, turning men into fountains of blood, spouting spouting spouting until Heaven itself drew back before the frothing red ocean.

But the Liberal and his Negro sycophants would've cried, Vengeance accomplishes nothing. You are only acting like your oppressor and such an act makes you no better than him. John Brown, his hands and wrists slick with blood, would've said, oh so softly and so quietly, Mere Vengeance is folly. Purgation is necessity.

Now it is over. America has had chance after chance to show that it really meant "that all men are endowed with certain inalienable rights." America has had precious chances in this decade to make it come true. Now it is over. The days of singing freedom songs and the days of combating bullets and billy clubs with Love. We Shall Overcome (and we have overcome our blindness) sounds old, out-dated and can enter the pantheon of the greats along with the IWW songs and the union songs. As one SNCC veteran put it after the Mississippi March, "Man, the people are too busy getting ready to fight to bother with singing anymore." And as for Love? That's always been better done in bed than on the picket line and marches. Love is fragile and gentle and seeks a like response. They used to sing "I Love Everybody" as they ducked bricks and bottles. Now they sing

> Too much love,
> Too much love,
> Nothing kills a niggler like
> Too much love.

They know, because they still get headaches from the beatings they took while love, love, loving. They know, because they died on those highways and in those jail cells, died from trying to change the hearts of men who had none. They know, the ones who have bleeding ulcers when they're twenty-three and the ones who have to have the eye operations. They know that nothing kills a nigger like too much love.

At one time black people desperately wanted to be American, to communicate with whites, to live in the Beloved Community. Now that is irrelevant. They know that it can't be until whites want it to be and it is obvious now that whites don't want it.

Does all of this mean that every American white is now a potential victim for some young Nat Turner? Does it mean the time is imminent when the red blood of blue-eyed, blonde-haired beauties will glisten on black arms and hands?

For many black people, the time is imminent. For others it simply means the white man no longer ixists. He is not to be lived with and he is not to be destroyed. He is simply to be ignored, because the time has come for the black man to control the things which effect his life. Like the Irish control Boston, the black man will control Harlem. For so long the black man lived his life in reaction to whites. Now he will live it only within the framework of his own blackness and his blackness links him with the Indians of Peru, the miner in Bolivia, the African and the freedom fighters of Vietnam. What they fight for is what the American black man fights for --- the right to govern his own life. If the white man interprets that to mean hatred, it is only a reflection of his own fears and anxieties and black people leave him to deal with it. There is too much to do to waste time and energy hating white people.

The old order passes away. Like the black riderless horse, boots turned the wrong way in the stirrups, following the coffin down the boulevard, it passes away. But there are no crowds to watch as it passes. There are no crowds, to mourn, to weep. No eulogies to read and no eternal flame is lit over the grave. There is no time for there are streets to be cleaned, houses painted and clothes washed. Everything must be scoured clean. Trash has to be thrown out. Garbage dumped and everything unfit, burned.

> The new order is coming, child.
> The old is passing away.

Julius Lester
Atlanta, Georgia
August 8, 1966

This originally appeared as an article entitled "The Angry Children of Malcolm X", SING OUT!, Oct/Nov 1966.

The Movement's Moving On

Tune Traditional - "John Brown's Body"
Words - Len Chandler, Jr.
© 1965 Fall River Music, Inc.

Mine eyes have seen injustice in each city, town and state
Your jails are filled with black men and your courts are white with hate
And with every bid for freedom someone whispers to us, "Wait."
That's why we keep marching on

CHORUS:

Move on over or we'll move on over you
Move on over or we'll move on over you
Move on over or we'll move on over you
And the movement's moving on

You conspire to keep us silent in the field and in the slum
You promise us the vote and sing us, "We Shall Overcome"
But John Brown knew what freedom was and died to win us some
That's why we keep marching on.

Chorus

Your dove of peace with bloody beak sinks talons in a child
You bend the olive branch to make a bow, then with a smile
You string it with the lynch rope you've been hiding all the while
That's why we keep marching on.

Chorus

It is you who are subversive, you're the killers of the dream
In a savage world of bandits it is you who are extreme
You never take your earmuffs off nor listen when we scream
That's why we keep marching on.

Chorus

I declare my independence from the fool and from the knave
I declare my independence from the coward and the slave
I declare that I will fight for right and fear no jail nor grave
That's why we keep marching on

Chorus

Many noble dreams are dreamed by small and voiceless man
Many noble deeds are done the righteous to defend
We're here today, John Brown, to say we'll triumph in the end
That's why we keep marching on

Chorus

PHOTO CREDITS